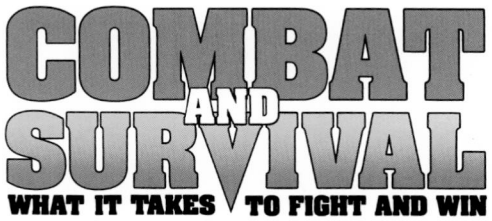

VOLUME
6

Originally published in the United Kingdom in weekly parts **COMBAT & SURVIVAL** is a study of the armed forces at work. It shows the skills taught to soldiers and the way in which military units operate. It examines the weapons and equipment used by different armies; and, by looking at recruit training and exercises, **COMBAT & SURVIVAL** demonstrates how the armed forces develop individual responsibility, leadership and initiative.

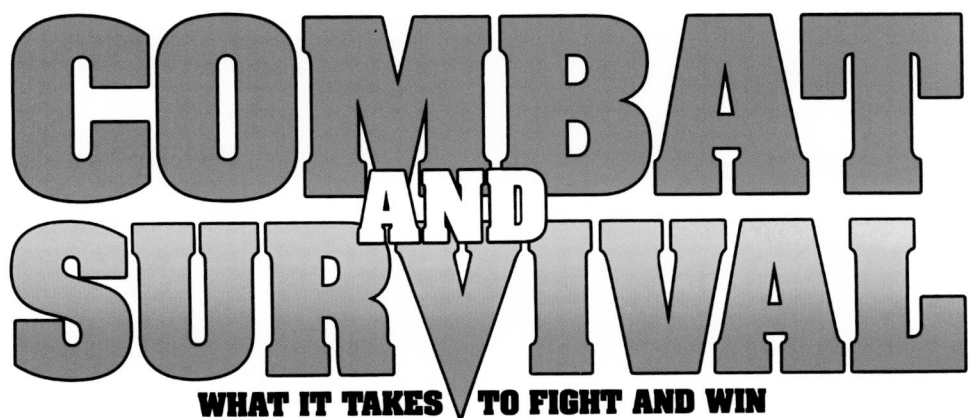

COMBAT AND SURVIVAL

WHAT IT TAKES TO FIGHT AND WIN

VOLUME
6

H. S. STUTTMAN, INC. *publishers*   Westport, Connecticut 06889

Contents
Volume 6

Published by H. S. STUTTMAN INC.
Westport, Connecticut 06889
© Aerospace Publishing 1991
ISBN 0-87475-560-3

RIDING INTO BATTLE

Modern armoured forces are a combined team, with tanks and infantry fighting in close co-operation. The infantrymen ride into action in Armoured Personnel Carriers which can keep pace with the tanks; sometimes you will fight from the vehicle, but in most situations you dismount to fight on foot. Certainly, the mechanised infantry platoon with its four APCs has far greater freedom of movement and can respond far quicker than 'leg' infantry. This section, taken from the US Army Field Manual FM 7-7, introduces you to mechanized warfare in the M113 APC, the combat vehicle of the US infantry.

Built from a special aluminium alloy that keeps the all-up weight down to less than 11 tonnes fully loaded, the APC gives its occupants protection from most small-arms fire and from grenade and shell fragments, but not from anti-tank guns, missiles and rockets. This means that the infantry leader must think very hard about when and how to dismount his troops and use them in the traditional foot soldiers' role.

In attack, the leader will try to fight from the vehicles for as long as possible, using the tactics worked out in advance for just this sort of situation, and will only get his men out of the protection of the APCs when he gets into close terrain like trees and bushes or comes up against obstacles or a strong anti-tank force.

This flexibility — to fight from vehicles with armour strong enough to deflect small-arms fire or to dismount

An Armoured Personnel Carrier enables you to move swiftly, keeping up with tanks. These US M113s carry the increased machine-gun armament adopted during the Vietnam War: a .50-cal Browning at the front, and an M60 7.62-mm machine-gun on each side.

6 BASIC RULES OF MOVEMENT

1. Make use of terrain that hides you from enemy observation or fire.
2. Avoid silhouetting your vehicle by crossing a skyline or moving directly forward from a hull-down position.
3. Cross open areas of ground as fast as you can.
4. Use your smoke grenade-launchers to cover disengagement or to protect a halted APC.
5. Move with a small force scouting ahead and with the rest of your team following behind.
6. Make sure your leading team can be covered by the vehicles behind.

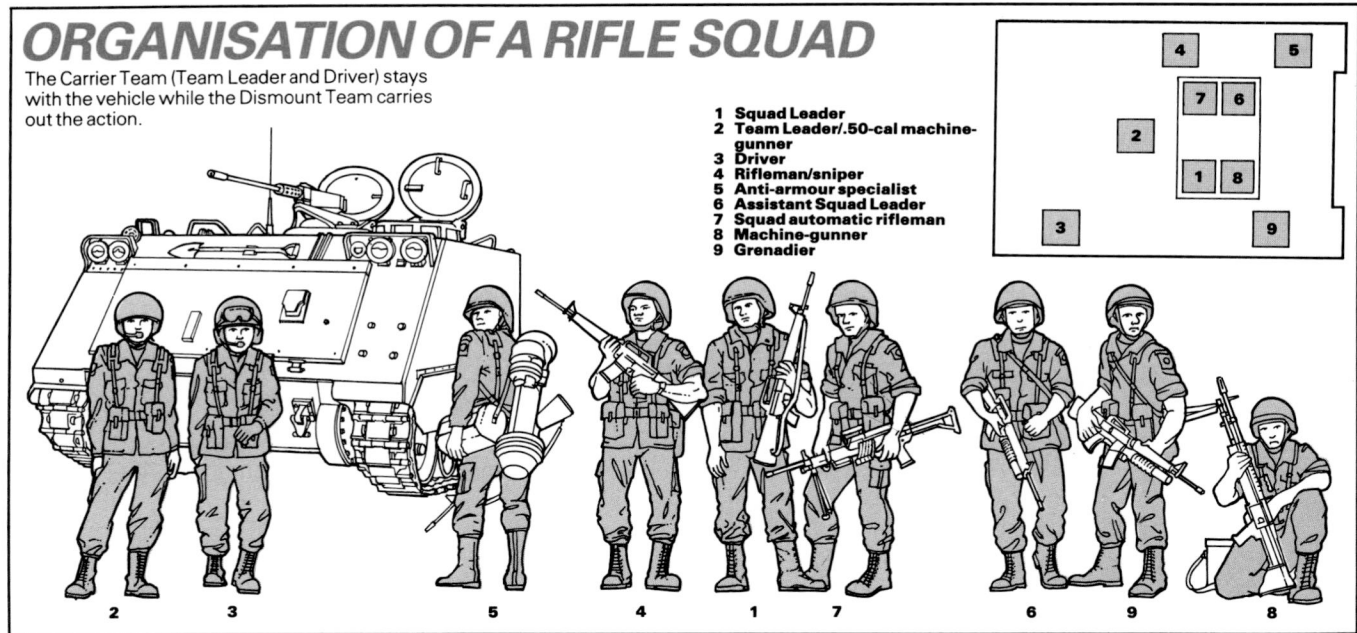

ORGANISATION OF A RIFLE SQUAD

The Carrier Team (Team Leader and Driver) stays with the vehicle while the Dismount Team carries out the action.

1 Squad Leader
2 Team Leader/.50-cal machine-gunner
3 Driver
4 Rifleman/sniper
5 Anti-armour specialist
6 Assistant Squad Leader
7 Squad automatic rifleman
8 Machine-gunner
9 Grenadier

and take on anti-armour forces with conventional infantry tactics, then perhaps call up the APCs, mount up again and carry on the advance as before – has meant that a new way of infantry fighting has had to be developed, but still within the age-old system of the five basic rules of combat:

1 Secure
2 Move
3 Shoot
4 Communicate
5 Sustain

When dismounting, the driver should place the vehicle in a covered position while the gunner provides suppressive fire with the .50-cal machine-gun. The dismount team exits to the right or left at the Squad Leader's command.

Make your position secure

The APC is 2½ metres tall and 5 metres long, so you have to choose lying-up and ambush positions with a lot of thought about how you're going to conceal it, both by means of natural cover and by applying camouflage.

Hollows in the ground, buildings and courtyards and patches of mature undergrowth and young trees (which are vulnerable to the vehicle itself if you have to take off in a hurry) are all likely locations.

Because you can't 'stand-to' an APC in just a second or two as you can an infantry fighting unit, it's especially important to get your local security well established. Reconnoitre the area very carefully before committing yourself to a location, and keep the

patrol activity up all the time the vehicles are in position.

Static sentry positions should be further out than normal, and this may make for a communications problem.

Remember, when selecting sites for individual vehicles, that you're not just parking them. They should be able to support and defend each other and the dismounted troops that are put out to defend them. For mounted infantry to be really effective, the men and the machines have to be working together as a team.

Move fast

Just like any infantry formation, APC-mounted infantry rely a lot on the principle of fire and movement – the squad divides into two; one part puts down fire while the other moves, then they change jobs, and so on.

But there are two main differences when you're using an APC – its heavy .50 calibre machine-gun can operate at longer range, and the movement takes place at 10 times the speed. The squad leader – and the team leaders, who now become vehicle commanders as well – must make sure that these features of the APC are used to the full, and this means careful planning and preparation.

Just like tanks – and also anti-tank helicopters – APCs are best sited in 'hull-down' positions. All their armament is found on top of the vehicle, while the infantry riding in them uses a door at the rear to mount and dismount.

Obviously, if the troops can get in and out while protected from enemy

fire, the whole operation will be a great deal safer. If the vehicles can move in the hull-down position as well – along roads or tracks with hedges and banks on each side, for example – then they are very difficult to detect, even when moving. This adds very considerably to their effectiveness, but gives them less room to deploy in case of attack.

Unit commanders must consider all these points when using the APC in attack. The extra speed of the vehicle gives you every chance of over-running enemy positions – especially if they've been careless in their anti-armour preparations – but it also means that it's easy to over-extend, to get so far in front that the advance becomes a series of isolated fire-fights that do little or nothing to really gain ground, and where you're in every danger of being surrounded and cut off.

On foot, infantrymen can fire and move as the need arises. In vehicles, the whole operation has to have a little more planning involved in it, though the excellent specification of the M113 Armoured Personnel carrier does make it surprisingly flexible. It can span trenches and ditches nearly two metres wide, and climb up 60-degree slopes.

Keep in touch

Communications between vehicles often require a radio net. As well as the sets fixed into the APC, the platoon commander, the platoon sergeant and each team leader will have personal radio transceivers. This means that communications are usually better between members of a mounted infantry unit than between foot soldiers in a squad, again making for better mobility and quicker response times.

It does make for one added danger, however – the enemy may be able to listen in to your transmissions. If he does he will not only gain intelligence, but also be able to pin-point your position.

As well as sophisticated radios, APC-mounted troops also have a wide range of STANO (Surveillance, Target Acquisition, Night Observation) devices available – Binoculars and AN/PAS-6 Metascopes for general observation, the M19 Infra-red Periscope for the driver, and AN/PVS and AN/TVS sights for the various different weapons.

Sustaining the attack

Because APCs are at risk from even hand-held anti-tank weapons, it's

PLATOON FORMATIONS

Column formation

This is the most frequently used formation, it is the best for road marches, movement in limited visibility or when passing through woods and defiles. You can deploy quickly into other formations and it is the easiest to control.

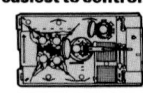
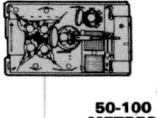

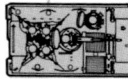

3

PLATOON SERGEANT

50-100 METRES

PLATOON LEADER

50-100 METRES

1

Signals for turning

ARM AND HAND SIGNAL: Turn left

FLAG SIGNAL: Turn left (The flag is green on one side and yellow on the other: green = turn left, yellow = turn right)

RADIO SIGNAL: "Lima, this is Lima Two-Six, left turn, out."

PLATOON LEADER

PLATOON SERGEANT

3   **1**

Line formation

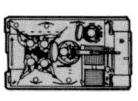

ARM AND HAND SIGNAL

FLAG SIGNAL

This is used when assaulting an objective, crossing open areas, exiting a wood or when emerging through a smokescreen. It gives maximum firepower to the front and is the best way in which to rapidly cross an open area.

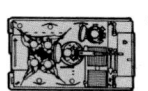
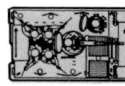
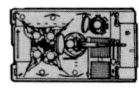
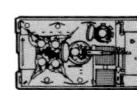

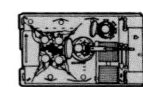

Echelon formation

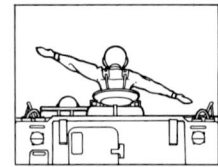

ARM AND HAND SIGNAL

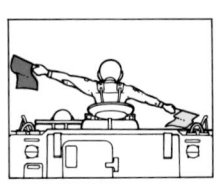

FLAG SIGNAL

Use echelon when you are on an exposed flank. It gives you excellent firepower to both the front and both flanks.

50-100 METRES

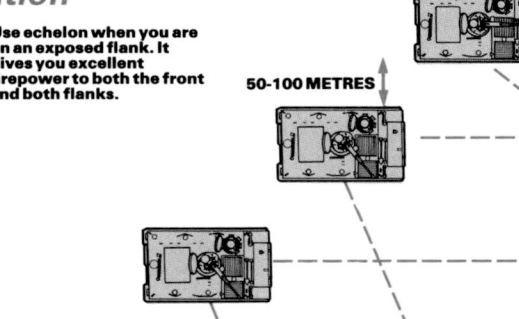
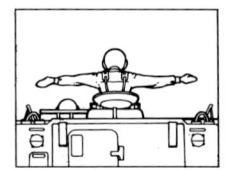
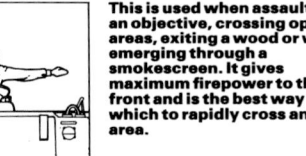
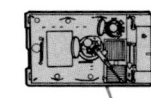

Vee formation

Use this when the situation is unclear and you want the unit concentrated with all-round firepower.

ARM AND HAND SIGNAL

FLAG SIGNAL

Wedge formation

This is easy to control and is simply a line with the flanking vehicles echeloned back. It is also used when the situation is unclear and you may need to deploy to either flank.

ARM AND HAND SIGNAL

FLAG SIGNAL

ALTERNATE SIGNAL

1

PLATOON LEADER

50-100 METRES

50-100 METRES

PLATOON SERGEANT

3

Herringbone formation

This is adopted by a column when it needs to deploy quickly, e.g. if ambushed or facing an enemy air attack. It proved very effective in Vietnam.

3

1

ARM AND HAND SIGNAL

PLATOON SERGEANT

PLATOON LEADER

Coil formation

Coil is a stationary formation providing all-round defence. It is used for refuelling, resupply and giving orders. It should not be used for very long in daylight as it presents a concentrated target.

Method 1
In poor visibility the platoon leader leads the vehicles round in a circle. When the ring is complete, all APCs turn 90°.

PS

1

PL

3

Method 2
A quicker way is for the platoon leader to signal, move his APC into position, and stop. The other APCs then move into their assigned places.

PL

3

1

PS

ARM AND HAND SIGNAL

3

If an M113 strikes an anti-tank mine anyone inside is likely to be injured. These Australian troops are riding on top where they are safer from mines, but of course more vulnerable to enemy rifles.

most important to allow the enemy no time to re-group and get its anti-armour specialists into the fire-fight. The speed at which the M113 can move cross-country gives the mounted infantry unit commander an advantage here, but he is still just as concerned to keep a high rate of fire concentrated on enemy positions. Getting from place to place quickly is important, but it's still weight of fire that wins fire-fights.

New supplies

He has to think about re-supply, too – ammunition, food and one new factor: fuel for the vehicles. Get too far away from a supply point, and you could suddenly find yourself helpless, with your carriers out of fuel. At that point, all the advantages you've had suddenly turn into liabilities.

Though the M113 can carry 12 men, including its driver, the normal load is nine. When the infantry squad is mounted in the vehicle, offensive operations involve the .50 calibre machine-gun plus four members of the squad positioned in the open well at the back of the vehicle and armed with automatic weapons and grenade launchers – though the Platoon Commander may have changed the weapons mix to include TOW and LAW anti-armour missiles, depending on intelligence reports of the enemy strengths he's likely to meet.

As well as the heavy machine-gun (which may be taken off and used as a dismounted support weapon if necessary), there are vehicle mounts for the squad's own 7.62-mm calibre M60 machine-gun and for anti-tank weapons.

Where the troops dismount for a

short 'mopping up' operation, close to the vehicle, these heavier weapons are often left with the APC, their operators arming themselves with more appropriate semi-automatic weapons instead.

Deadly missiles

The APC's worst enemy is the Anti-Tank Guided Missile (ATGM), now so light and compact that you must expect even small units of enemy troops to be equipped with them. Missiles such as these have one big weakness: they don't work well if there are obstacles – trees, for example, or even wire fences – between the launcher and the target. In open country, though, they're deadly.

It is the APC's driver who is the vehicle's first line of defence against ATGMs. His skill at using the shape of the country to keep the vehicle out of the sight-line of enemy troops, and his ability to keep the vehicle moving through difficult patches instead of cutting across open country, make all the difference.

Terrain driving, as it is called, is

A combined arms team of M48 tanks and M113 APCs halts at the edge of a forest and the dismount teams prepare to assault on foot. In Vietnam armoured forces proved more effective than expected in jungle.

practised over and over until it becomes second nature following four very basic guidelines:

1 Use all available cover.
2 Avoid the skyline.
3 Cross even small open areas fast.
4 Don't move straight forward out of a hull-down firing position.

Even though all but the last of these are basic skills that every infantryman learns, the way they're put into prac-

tice is changed a lot by the size and speed of the vehicles. Reading the terrain, whether from the map or from looking directly at the ground, becomes even more important than ever before.

DISMOUNTED OPERATIONS

When the dismount teams operate on foot the APCs can use their machine guns to provide covering fire. The teams may dismount in situations below.

1 To fight in woods or built up areas which restrict the movement of vehicles.

2 When the APC's movement is blocked by enemy anti-tank weapons.

3 To assault or clear an objective.

4 To clear obstacles

5 To deploy Dragon anti-tank missiles.

6 To move on a different route while the APCs provide fire support.

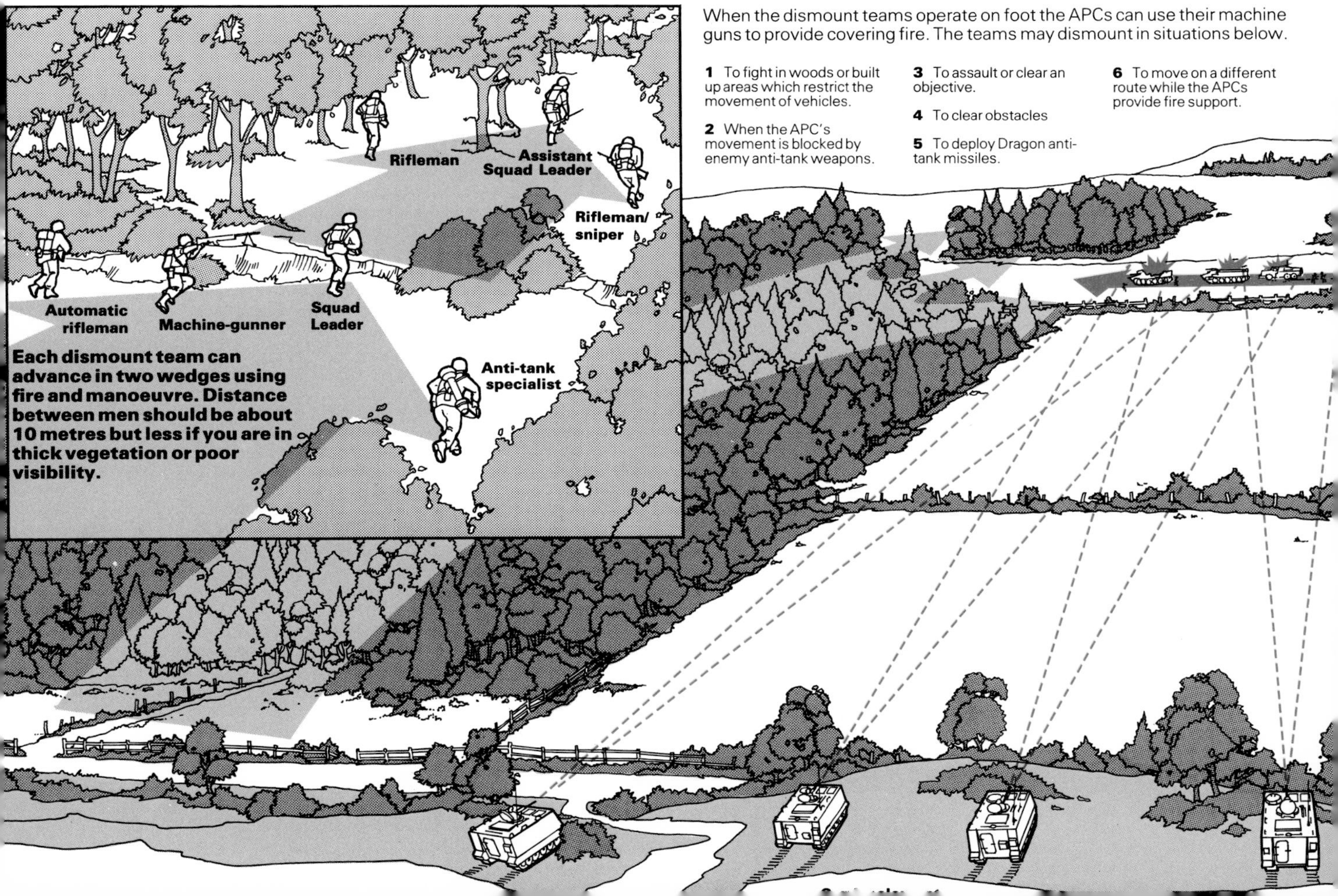

Rifleman

Assistant Squad Leader

Rifleman/ sniper

Automatic rifleman

Machine-gunner

Squad Leader

Anti-tank specialist

Each dismount team can advance in two wedges using fire and manoeuvre. Distance between men should be about 10 metres but less if you are in thick vegetation or poor visibility.

Combat Report
Mayotte:
French Foreign Legion Patrol Part 1

John James Claxton, a former member of the French Foreign Legion, describes 10 minutes of action that followed 10 weeks of patrolling.

In August 1982 I was serving with the First Troop, Fourth Squadron of the First Foreign Legion Cavalry Regiment, when we were tasked to the island of Mayotte, part of the Comoro Islands, in the Indian Ocean.

It was to be a four-month tour, and most of us were expecting four months in the sun with the odd march, and maybe the odd parade.

The island of Mayotte is strategically well placed. It has a good airport within flying distance of most African states, and it has an oil storage depot to refuel French warships. This is permanently guarded by Legionnaires, who are also there to uphold the 'French way of life'.

After seeing off the outgoing Legion unit, one troop went to the jungle camp at Kwale on the main island and two troops stayed in the main camp on the island of Dzaoudzi. I went to Kwale with the first troop. We were to spend a month there patrolling the main island, doing section drills, working to improve the camp, and all the general mundane jobs soldiers the world over love to hate.

A fighting patrol

In late September I was sent on an NCO cadre course at Majambini, a very secluded place in the mountains of the main island. We were to stay in what had been a Governor's weekend mansion, but it was very run down and it took us two weeks to make it fit for occupation. We used all the natural resources, mainly bamboo, and built a cookhouse, storage huts, an assault course and even a jail. In between we had to mount guard, eat, clean up, and do PT and all other general duties, and this was before we even started the course!

During this time some demonstrations and rioting broke out on the main island, so the alert was stepped up and our guards doubled. In October we were in camp doing unarmed combat when the camp came under mortar attack: three rounds in total – not many, but it had us all running for cover.

As always, we had our personal weapons with us, so we headed straight for our defensive positions and awaited further developments. When everything had calmed down, including us, we surveyed the damage, which (apart from the cookhouse) was minimal. We then sent out a fighting patrol, of which I was part, to see if we could locate any sign of enemy activity.

Most of us expected four pleasant months in the sunshine when we were posted to the Indian Ocean.

We knew we could be heading straight for an ambush, so we moved very carefully in the dense jungle. We spent most of the time listening for movement but there was none so, as night fell, we moved back into camp, had some scran and cleaned our weapons and ourselves.

That night the camp was put into total darkness and the guards had a jumpy time, with every bush and tree moving and looking like people.

In the morning another fighting patrol went out to check the area, and again there was nothing to be seen or heard. They day was spent digging new trenches and setting anti-personnel mines and trip flares in front of our positions. Plans were also being drawn up for wider-ranging patrols and ambushes, and if need be for patrols to stay out for very long periods until whoever attacked us was hunted down and captured or killed. And so began the 10 weeks of hunting that ended in 10 minutes of action.

The mortar that had been used against us was rumoured to be in an area called Chungi, so we were tasked to locate it. Chungi was three days' march from our base. The main plan was to move into the area and to set up ambushes. We loaded up our packs with rations, ammo, grenades, mines, radios and first aid kits, and set off for the area.

There was the crack of a twig

Our first objective was Kwale, where there was already one of our troops, but we were heading for a position about four kilometres north of the camp by a crossing point on the river Kwale, where we would set up an ambush for the night.

In the afternoon of the first day there was a downpour that made the track slippery and very muddy, and when we stopped we were all steaming. We were also very tense; the enemy could be waiting for us along the track, so our trackers Gimenez and Symaniak were well ahead of us, leaving signs to let us know that everything was okay ahead.

By early evening we arrived at our objective, and set about building a position for our machine-gun overlooking the track down to the river crossing so that it could be manned during the night. Then we cooked something to eat, fixed a guard rota and got our head down.

My mate Tony Carlton and I had the midnight till two o'clock guard stag. When it was our turn we took over and settled down. We were lying there, quietly chatting about what we were going to do when we got back to France (a favourite subject!), when there was a crack of a twig or branch that brought us to full alert.

We peered on to the track to see what was moving about. Something caught my eye to the right of the river and I pointed it out to Tony. He moved behind the machine gun and I prepared a flare, but decided against using it as we didn't yet know it was the enemy.

We decided to wake up the sergeant. He told me to watch whoever it was and, if they got too close, to use whatever force we thought necessary. I went back to the position and we lay there waiting to see what would happen.

Whoever it was kept their distance, but made sure we knew he was there. I was glad when the guard duty finished and we were relieved. We briefed the new sentries and made our way back to our sleeping bags. I fell into an uneasy sleep, expecting to hear gunfire at any moment.

The coast was clear

Before first light we had a stand-to, just in case whoever was out there decided to come in and have a go at us. Once the sun came up, a small fighting patrol was sent out to see if there was anyone about. They found nothing, but we now realised that we were expected and that we wouldn't have everything our own way.

We cleared up the camp and got ready to move out, but now everyone had to be that little bit more alert. As we now expected to be ambushed at any time we kept on the move until midday, when we stopped and had a brew-up and a bite to eat.

The word was passed around to move out in 10 minutes. I was told by the sergeant that it was my turn to carry the radio which, on its own, weighed 10 kilos. I had to re-arrange my pack to fit it in, and when I put it back on it was like carrying a sack of lead. Once I was ready, off we went. The first hour was uncomfortable and I was sweating like a pig, but I soon got used to the weight. I was worried, though, in case we had to leg it from an ambush: would I have the strength to run?

In mid-afternoon two of the Section went forward and had a look around. The coast was clear, and we crossed over and took up some fire positions while we decided what to do next. We radioed the scouts who had gone on ahead and arranged a place where we could meet and have something to eat and drink and, due to the heat, a bit of a siesta. They said they had found an ideal place that was easy to defend, so we set off.

We arrived about an hour later and set about making the scoff and preparing a defensive position. We had a light snack, put a couple of sentries out and got our heads down.

Our unarmed combat was tough, but we did not expect mortar fire during the practice session.

TAKING THE HIGH GROUND

Your armoured personnel carrier is bullet-proof and protects you from shell splinters, but an anti-tank missile will smash through its thin armour with horrific consequences. When on the move you must scan the ground ahead for possible killing grounds where enemy anti-tank teams are lying in wait and use the principles of fire and movement, one APC covering another.

The US Army's Field Manual FM 7-7 gives three standard strategies for APC movement. The one you select depends on the strength of your chances of making contact with the enemy.

Although this 'contact status' determines which of the three movement strategies will be used, you as platoon commander must consider the terrain and the job to be done when deciding which of the five movement formations the mounted infantry unit will adopt.

In theory, any one of them can be used in any of the three contact statuses, though in Conditions Two and Three this can be done only by splitting the platoon into two parts or by joining up with another of the Company's platoons.

1 Travelling: single-unit movement

When contact with the enemy is thought to be unlikely, your APC formation moves as a single unit, without splitting up into two elements that protect and cover each other. Because speed across the ground and control are the two most important factors, the column movement formation is used most often.

The unit is not likely to have to go into action, and it's important to keep moving as fast as possible, so the platoon commander will generally take the point position. You will use hand and arm signals to indicate the direction that the unit is to take, and also to signal changes of formation.

The APC's rear door is left open, and one member of the squad is detailed to maintain a watch on the vehicle following, reporting to you if he loses contact.

Travelling in this way, each of the

3 MOVEMENT STRATEGIES

1. Travelling
Used when contact with the enemy is unlikely.

2. Travelling Overwatch
Used when there is a possibility of contact with the enemy.

3. Bounding Overwatch
Used when contact with the enemy is expected or likely.

Because of the range and power of modern weapons, a moving unit needs to have a scout element well ahead of the main body of vehicles to detect the enemy before the whole unit is in range of their weapons. Here a squad of the US 11th Armored Cavalry scans the ground ahead in Vietnam.

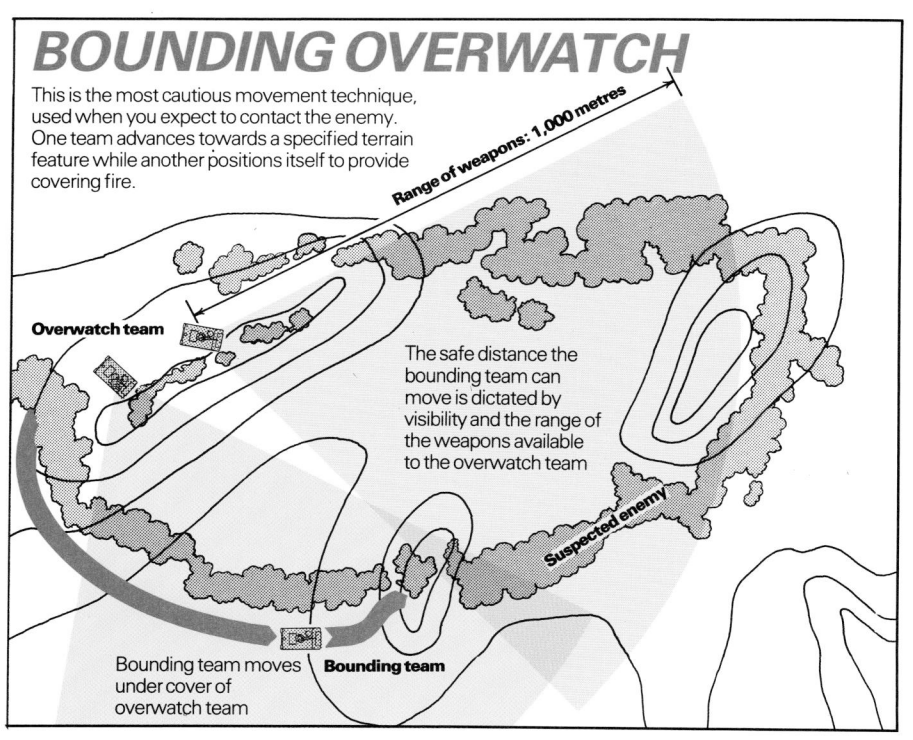

BOUNDING OVERWATCH

This is the most cautious movement technique, used when you expect to contact the enemy. One team advances towards a specified terrain feature while another positions itself to provide covering fire.

Range of weapons: 1,000 metres

Overwatch team

The safe distance the bounding team can move is dictated by visibility and the range of the weapons available to the overwatch team

Suspected enemy

Bounding team moves under cover of overwatch team

Bounding team

platoon's vehicles is responsible for observation and first-line security in one sector. The lead vehicle looks out ahead; the second vehicle, which is staggered to the right in column formation, to the right; the third to the left; and the fourth to the rear.

Sometimes it becomes necessary to travel with the troops dismounted from the vehicles, though this is unusual because contact with the enemy is unlikely in Condition One. If it does become necessary, you will generally dismount with your men while the platoon sergeant, your second-in-command, stays with the vehicles.

2 Travelling Overwatch: two-part movement

The second stage of readiness is called Travelling Overwatch. This technique splits the travelling force into two parts, a small spear-head group and a larger overwatch force, and requires them both to position themselves so that the larger force can cover and protect the other all the time.

ADVANCE TO CONTACT

Your job as platoon leader is to make certain that everyone knows what to do before the movement begins. You need to make clear: (**1**) What is known about the enemy situation; (**2**) The next overwatch position: this is where the bounding team will halt; (**3**) The route of the bounding team to the next overwatch position; (**4**) What you intend to do when they have got there; (**5**) Target reference point and sectors of fire.

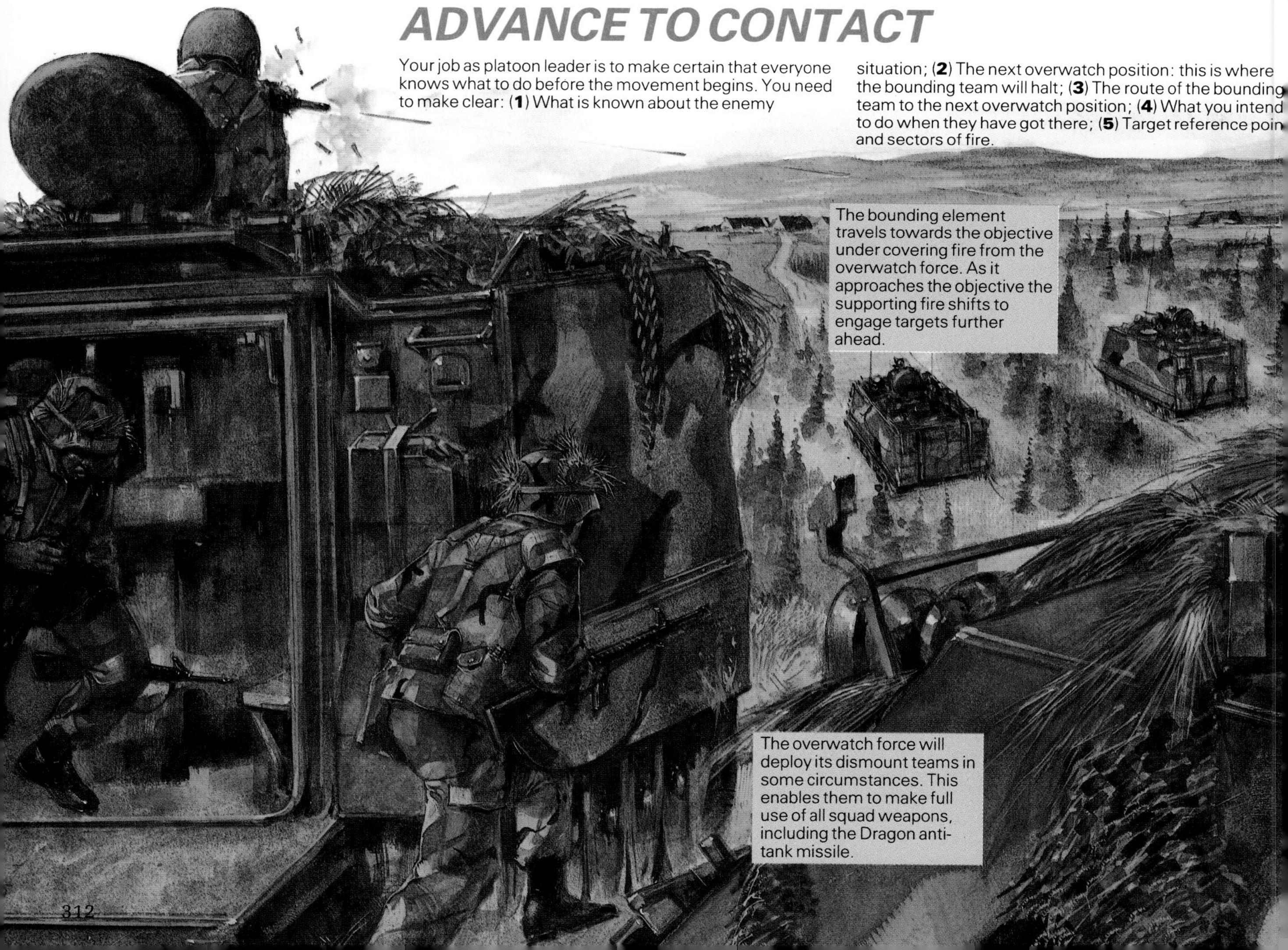

The bounding element travels towards the objective under covering fire from the overwatch force. As it approaches the objective the supporting fire shifts to engage targets further ahead.

The overwatch force will deploy its dismount teams in some circumstances. This enables them to make full use of all squad weapons, including the Dragon anti-tank missile.

The lie of the land, together with whatever information about enemy positions and strengths that's available, will decide which movement formation your unit will take up. By definition, it won't be the line formation, but any one of the other four may be used.

Moving into country that may conceal enemy forces is part normal advance and part patrol activity. It's important to keep the forward movement going, but at the same time you must present the enemy with as small a target as possible – if he can be persuaded to attack a single vehicle, he gives away his position without being able to do much good for himself in the process.

Because you must be in a position to control all four of your vehicles, you drop back to number two position in the movement formation in Travelling Overwatch, and send the lead vehicle out 400 to 600 metres ahead, staying in visual and radio contact all the time.

Because its armour will withstand anything less than an Anti-Tank Guided Missile, the APC is well suited to this decoy role. If it does succeed in drawing enemy fire, the heavy .50 calibre machine-guns mounted on the platoon's vehicles

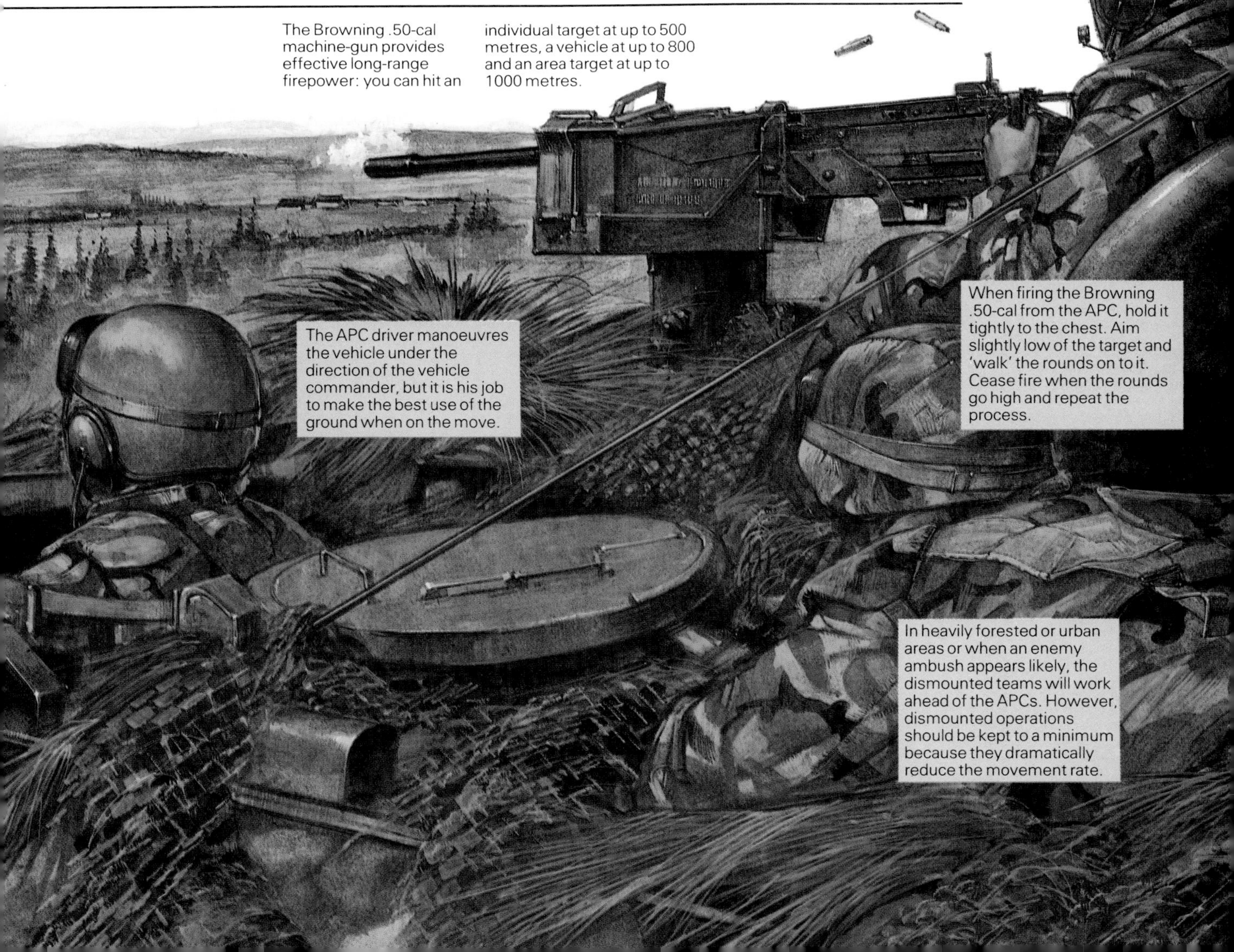

Distance between vehicles varies according to the terrain. In this Vietnamese jungle, the APCs have to keep very close indeed to be able to see each other and thus provide covering fire.

The Browning .50-cal machine-gun provides effective long-range firepower: you can hit an individual target at up to 500 metres, a vehicle at up to 800 and an area target at up to 1000 metres.

When firing the Browning .50-cal from the APC, hold it tightly to the chest. Aim slightly low of the target and 'walk' the rounds on to it. Cease fire when the rounds go high and repeat the process.

The APC driver manoeuvres the vehicle under the direction of the vehicle commander, but it is his job to make the best use of the ground when on the move.

In heavily forested or urban areas or when an enemy ambush appears likely, the dismounted teams will work ahead of the APCs. However, dismounted operations should be kept to a minimum because they dramatically reduce the movement rate.

HULL DOWN TO ENEMY FIRE

Occupying a hull-down position simply means positioning the vehicle so that its hull is behind cover and cannot be hit by enemy weapons. However, the vehicle's own weapons are above the cover and able to fire at the enemy.

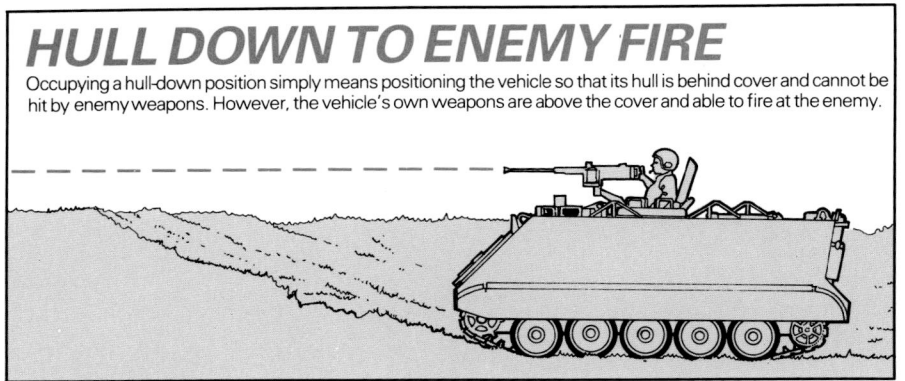

DAY SIGNALS

Arm and hand signals are the basic way of communicating within squads and platoons in conditions of good visibility. Because of the dangers of misunderstood signals it is important that everyone practises these signal techniques regularly. The bottom row of signals is performed by the vehicle's crew members.

I am ready

I do not understand

Assemble

Disregard previous command

Enemy in sight

Attention

Commence firing

Cease firing

Cover our move

Move out

Form line

Enemy in sight

---

will stand a very good chance of winning a fire-fight even at ranges of up to 1,000 metres, and the distance involved will give them every chance to reform into the most effective grouping possible in order to mount an assault.

Moving while dismounted

Even though the object of the exercise is to move forward as fast as possible, it may sometimes be necessary to move using the Travelling Overwatch technique with the platoon dismounted from the vehicles, especially if you suspect that the enemy forces may have their anti-armour specialists deployed.

In this case the lead section will take the place of the lead vehicle, and will stay in closer contact with the rest of the platoon – perhaps 100 metres in front. The vehicles must keep to positions where they can cover both the lead section and the rest of the dismounted element.

Remember, both these techniques – Travelling and Travelling Overwatch – have the same objective: to advance on an objective as fast as possible. Separating the men from their vehicles takes away the speed advantage that is the main part of the difference between Mounted Infantry and ordinary footsoldiers. Keep the men in the carriers. Dismount only when it's absolutely necessary.

3 Bounding Overwatch: fire and move

The third movement technique, called Bounding Overwatch, is used when contact with the enemy is ex-

STREET FIGHT

In built-up areas the dismount teams lead the way in a modified column formation, clearing the buildings as they go. As the column moves under covering fire from the APCs, each team makes sure there are no enemy in the buildings on its side of the street and keeps the upper floors of the buildings across the street under observation.

pected. The attacking force is split into two equal parts, the bounding force and the overwatch force, and are used in a way very similar to the traditional infantryman's fire-and-move tactics.

Bounding overwatch is the most deliberate and cautious of the three movement techniques. While the other two assume that the enemy may be about, and arrange the unit to counter any move he may make, Bounding Overwatch assumes that the enemy is definitely there waiting to attack. The other two put speed first, but the Bounding Overwatch is designed to make the operation as safe as possible for the troops and vehicles taking part.

Approaching the enemy
The overwatch force covers the bounding force from a static position that offers a good field of fire against possible enemy operations. How far the bounding force will go is decided in advance. The sort of things that you will look for when selecting a target site depends on which of two types of movement you use at the time. These could be:
1 Successive advance, where the overwatch force moves up to the positions that the bounding force has just established, takes them over and covers the next movement of the

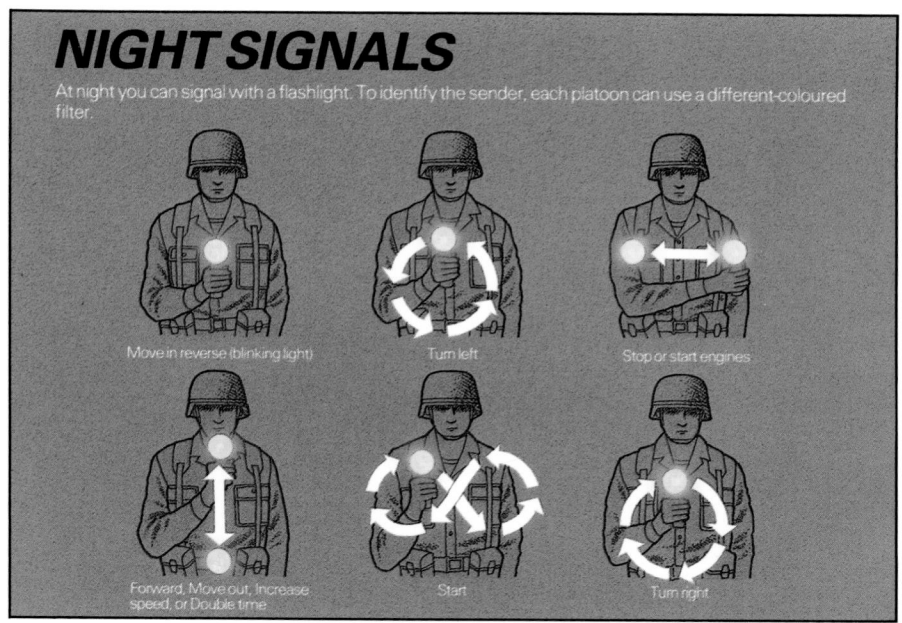

NIGHT SIGNALS

At night you can signal with a flashlight. To identify the sender, each platoon can use a different-coloured filter.

Move in reverse (blinking light) Turn left Stop or start engines

Forward, Move out, Increase speed, or Double time Start Turn right

bounding force.
2 Alternate advance, where the overwatch force moves forward through and past the area where the bounding force has come to a halt, and takes on the job of the bounding force itself.

The length of each bound is limited by the effective range of the weapons available, by the fields of fire that the

overwatch force can control, and by other, more artificial factors such as visibility in bad weather.

APCs enable the infantry to keep up with tanks, but sometimes the tanks have to lend a hand: here an M551 Sheridan tows an M113 through deep mud in Vietnam.

Combat Report
Mayotte:
French Foreign Legion Patrol Part 2

John James Claxton continues his story of an action by the French Foreign Legion on the Indian Ocean island of Mayotte in December 1982.

When I woke up the sun was beating down on my head and making me feel very groggy. The Sergeant decided that we could mount fighting patrols from our position, so we set about making the place more comfortable and strengthening its defences.

We had a look at the map and saw that there was a village about five kilometres away. It was decided to go down and show our faces and let it be known that there weren't too many of us, so that the enemy would be tempted to attack us or come looking for us.

We left behind a rear guard and set off, looking for ambush positions on the way. We would have liked to mine the tracks but, as the locals used them, it wouldn't have been a good idea!

When we arrived at the village, we found the locals a little apprehensive. We stayed about half an hour, hinting that we were the only ones in the area. Then we left, taking a different route back to camp to avoid any ambush.

We knew that we would be followed, so after about a kilometre we stopped and waited. After 10 minutes two young lads came along and we jumped them, frightening the life out of them. We asked why they were following us and they said they were ''just going for a walk''. To stop them going off and informing the enemy of our whereabouts we tied them to a tree, next to the track so it wouldn't be too long before they were rescued.

Preparing the ambush

We arrived safely back at camp. Scoff was arranged and a guard rota worked out. We then discussed our plans for the next day. We searched the map for possible ambush positions: river crossings, track junctions, outskirts of the villages. There were so many we couldn't decide where to wait, so it was planned to send out a fighting patrol to one of the positions who would wait during daylight hours to see if anyone came along.

It was on one of these patrols that we walked into an enemy group coming in the opposite direction. We were very lucky that our scouts were a good way in front of us and saw them coming across some open ground. They called us on the radio and we told them to head back towards us, as we hastily looked for a suitable site to prepare an ambush.

We had recently crossed a river, so we told the scouts to meet us there and headed back to it to prepare the ambush. We had the high ground, and set up the machine-guns so that they would overlap each other when firing.

The Sergeant said nobody was to fire until he did, so we just lay there. I realised how noisy the jungle was; it seemed to be moving, and the mozzies were attacking us in droves.

It was about 20 minutes before their scout came into view. As he approached the river Tony sighted his machine-gun on him.

He stopped at the river and crouched down to fill his water bottle. All the time he was looking around, and I thought he knew something was up. But he stood up, replaced his water bottle and came across and carried on down the track. We thought of jumping him, but then decided against it as it might mean missing the main prize.

He passed within 30 metres of me and Tony; he looked in our direction and just carried on down the track. We looked at each in disbelief. I was tingling with adrenalin, and found myself a little bit out of breath. It seemed ages before the main party came into view; in fact, it was about five minutes.

When they did arrive, I could count seven heavily-armed men quite close together. The Sergeant waited until the majority were in the process of crossing the river, then he let rip. A hail of gunfire exploded around them and the noise was deafening.

My rifle was empty

Most of them were caught in the open and the river. One tried to scramble up the bank into the jungle, but gunfire followed him until he rolled back down to the edge of the river. Two tried to fire back, but were soon cut down.

It was then that I heard firing coming from behind me. It was the scout coming back along the track spraying both sides and, as I was one of the closest to him, I thought I had better move as I was in danger of being shot. So I got up and ran up the hill, shouting to Tony to do the same. I don't know where he got to but I didn't see him until it was all over. Anyway, my main thought was keeping me eye on matey on the track!

When I thought I was in a good position I turned and saw him still coming, firing all the time. I sighted my rifle on him and squeezed the trigger and nothing happened. My rifle was empty. I had committed the cardinal sin – not counting my rounds!

I quickly reloaded and, as the bloke came level with me, I fired one round that hit him in the shoulder and spun him around. I then let loose a burst of fire that hit him in the upper chest and throat, and down he went. It just wasn't real. While I was firing I thought, 'Should I keep my head down,' but something overcame my fear and made me stand up and shoot. My mates were in danger, and I felt responsible for them; and anyway I was doing the job I was trained for.

Retrieving the bodies

By now the firing had subsided, and the Sergeant called out our names to see if anyone was hurt. Everyone shouted back, 'No injuries.' He then told us to come to his position, which was further up the hill from where I was. He left a few guys covering us and we moved down to the river to check if anyone had survived the exchange of fire. When I reached the river I looked at the bodies that were lying on the bank and in the water. They looked like pathetic rag dolls, but they were human beings.

We went into the river to retrieve the bodies and weapons. One body went down the river and took some time to bring back. I was amazed at the amount of blood; it was in pools around the bodies. One was shot up pretty bad, and his leg almost came off when we lifted him.

The Sergeant then came up and told us that we would have to stay the night until more men arrived to help us carry the bodies to the main road so that the police could try to identify them. So we moved the bodies away from the track and covered them up with a couple of ponchos. It was very hard to carry them – they just kept flopping all over the place. We then moved about 150 metres away and set about making a camp for the night. The guard position was set up about 50 metres from the bodies in case anyone came to retrieve them.

After all this I realised how hungry I was, but I found it hard to eat. I looked at Tony and he was sitting there cleaning his weapon, deep in

On patrol, carrying the AA52 light machine-gun. We wanted to mine the tracks but local villagers would probably have stepped on them, so this was not a practical possibility.

thought. I looked around at the men in my section and thought how well they had performed over the last ten weeks; heads down, and just getting on with the job. We had only done what we were expected to do: killed the enemy. Everything we had learned in the Legion told us to feel pride in that, and most of us did, but I could not understand why feelings of pity and guilt were mixed with that pride.

I knew I had acquired a great deal of affection for these Legionnaires simply because we had been through a lot together. These were the men I had shared the fear and excitement of battle with; the heat and the dust; tense, watchful nights; the risks of patrolling a desolate track. There were more admirable men in the world, more principled men, and men with finer sensibilities; but they slept in peaceful beds.

The base was a complete mess before the Legionnaires got to work on it. After two weeks it was in fine shape, until the enemy mortared it.

ADVANCE! ATTACK! ASSAULT!

The M113 Armoured Personnel Carrier, fast, agile and heavily armed, is a frightening weapon. Working together in company strength, just a dozen of them can deliver more than 100 fighting men into the thick of an attack quickly and in relative safety and support them with their own devastating fire power.

This section looks at the way APCs are used in attack, to assault enemy positions and destroy them in the shortest possible time. It is taken from the US Army's FM 7-7 Field Manual.

An attack can be split into two separate parts:
1 Movement to contact.
2 The assault itself.

Intelligence from patrols, airborne surveillance and perhaps interrogation of enemy prisoners will give the attack commander an idea of the positions the enemy is occupying, but things happen so quickly in battle that this information is only ever a starting point. Moving towards contact with the enemy, the attack commander wants to achieve two things: update his information, and get his troops into position safely and without giving away too much of his plan.

Clearing obstacles

Moving forward using the technique called Bounding Overwatch, the company's armoured vehicles support each other and the much heavier armour of the tank platoon, dismounting their infantrymen to clear obstacles and possible ambush sites and whenever they encounter difficult terrain such as woodland and buildings that can't be by-passed, and when visibility is poor. Their speed and

manoeuvrability allows them to get in, dispose of the obstacle, and get on with the advance with the least possible delay.

Movement to contact

The moment the leading element of the patrol or advance makes contact with the enemy it must react quickly and aggressively. The platoon's action in the first few seconds of the engage-

An APC platoon of the Israeli army prepares to move out: the squad commander joins the .50-calibre machine-gunner on top of the vehicle and other soldiers sit up to maintain all-round vision. Extra machine-guns are mounted on the vehicle sides; these are particularly valuable in disturbing the aim of an enemy anti-tank guided missile operator.

*Your squad's **M60** general-purpose machine-gun can be used either on its bipod or fixed to a tripod and used to provide sustained fire to cover an attack.*

ment may well determine whether the battle is lost or won.

The Platoon Commander has three objectives now:

1 Suppress enemy fire.
2 Deploy his forces.
3 Report the contact.

His first step is to assess the situation and make an estimate of the enemy's strength.

Quick attack

If enemy resistance is light, a hasty attack without further planning or reinforcement may be the best way to deal with it. Troops should be mounted in the vehicles wherever possible, so that they can be moved or redeployed quickly.

It may be, though, that the enemy doesn't present a real threat, and can be safely by-passed. It's important to keep the forward movement going, and so the company commander will probably use this option whenever he can, mopping up the enemy pocket later when there's more time.

Enemy contained

If there is strong enough enemy resistance to stop the lead platoon's forward movement, then they will have to be contained and suppressed. If this is the case, it may require the attention of the whole company together with

whatever support units, such as combat engineers, are available.

The assault

An attack generally has one of two objectives – to destroy or capture enemy troops or material, or to secure a key territorial feature. Accurate intelligence, training and equipment, and troop morale are all vitally important, but so is effective leadership – to assess the situation, organise the tactical plan, and communicate it to the men who are going to carry it out.

At a minimum, the plan has to cover five headings:

ADVANCING ALONG ROADS

A column of APCs moving down a road is very vulnerable to enemy anti-tank weapons, particularly where the road bends. When advancing to contact, send the dismount teams ahead to check out each corner.

2 Dismount teams clear the terrain on each side of the bend, starting with the high ground adjacent to the bend.

3 Once the dismount teams have cleared the terrain around the bend, they check the road and the banks for mines and booby-traps.

4 The APCs advance to new overwatch positions using bounding overwatch movement.

1 The APCs get into an overwatch position where they can cover as much of the bend as possible.

HOW THE PLATOON CROSSES A BRIDGE

Approach a bridge as a possible ambush site and clear it before crossing. Remember, the enemy may have weapons ranged in on the bridge, or may have booby-trapped the approaches or wired the whole structure for demolition.

2 If a fording site is available the dismount teams cross the river and secure the far side, occupying overwatch positions.

3 A carrier and its dismount team advance to the bridge and carefully examine the approaches and the bridge itself in case the enemy has mined them.

1 The APCs move into an overwatch position where they can cover the terrain on both flanks of the bridge and the far side.

1 Situation
2 Mission
3 Execution
4 Support
5 Communications

Nothing must be left to chance – or even assumed – at this point. The troops involved in the operation must all know their starting point, timetable and objectives, and there must be enough flexibility to take account of changes in the way enemy forces are deployed and the inevitable problems of troops sticking to the timetable as a result of resistance being more forceful than was anticipated.

Where enemy resistance is light, anti-armour weapons can be dealt with and the terrain allows easy movement, then the infantry will stay mounted in the vehicles.

Heavy armour

If a tank force is available, then the heavy armour will take the lead, laying down as dense a volume of fire as possible on to the enemy positions, with the APCs following two to four hundred metres behind, covering the flanks and rear of the tanks with heavy machine-gun fire.

If a stop order comes, the vehicles commander chooses a covered position with a good field of fire and continues to engage specific targets or lay down general suppressing fire.

Any halt at this stage will be short, so troops do not dismount to establish security for the vehicles, but should there be real danger from enemy anti-armour teams, the dismount order will come before the final assault is begun. It would be suicidal to stop the transport in the full face of enemy fire and dismount troops then.

As in any other circumstances, the dismount option is used during the final assault when enemy anti-tank weapons can't be suppressed, or when there are obstacles that will slow or halt the APCs. And, just as

before, the carrier element will be placed to give the best possible covering and suppressing fire, moving to an overwatching position from the point where the troops have been dropped if necessary.

The object of the final phase of the attack – the assault proper – is to lay down ferocious firepower into the enemy positions and then take them

The M113 armoured personnel carrier is fully amphibious, its tracks propelling it through the water. Before taking the plunge, switch on the two bilge pumps and set up the trim vane at the front.

physically if necessary, killing and capturing as many enemy personnel as possible and securing the maximum amount of equipment and material. The assault is not a mindless charge. It is a cautious yet bold and aggressive action, using all the principles of cover and concealment and fire and movement.

Resistant positions

The most hastily-prepared defensive positions can be surprisingly resistant to vehicles, even to tracked vehicles such as M113 APCs and tanks, and the attack commander must always be ready to dismount his troops and fight them as regular in-fantry. Even then, the heavy weapons and ammunition load that the APCs can carry can have a significant effect on the outcome of the assault.

The carrier element, now empty of all troops except for the driver and gunner and in one case the team leader, maintains heavy covering fire. This supporting fire needs to be close in to the dismount element, especially in the last stage of the assault, and so the gunners responsible must be very careful when selecting their aiming points so as not to endanger friendly forces.

The carrier element leader will mark the borders of fire zones, perhaps with tracer rounds, and also order smoke grenades where necessary. The dismount element will generate their own smoke as well, of course, and the dismount element leader will vary the colour of smoke used – yellow, green, red, for example – to signal to the carrier element that certain pre-arranged points have been reached so that supporting fire can be redirected.

Flexible overwatch

The overwatching position of the carrier element need not be firmly fixed. In fact, there will probably come a time during the assault when the vehicles will have to cease their supporting fire for fear of hitting their own dismounted men.

At that point they are free to move to a secondary overwatch position, from which they have a clearer view of the target and can re-start their support activity. In this way it may be

ASSAULTING THE OBJECTIVE

The assault is the last phase of the attack when the attacking force closes on the enemy position. It is not a 'charge' in the old-fashioned sense; you must use all available cover and concealment and the techniques of fire and movement. Using mutually supporting covering fire, you move on to and across the objective, destroying or capturing the enemy.

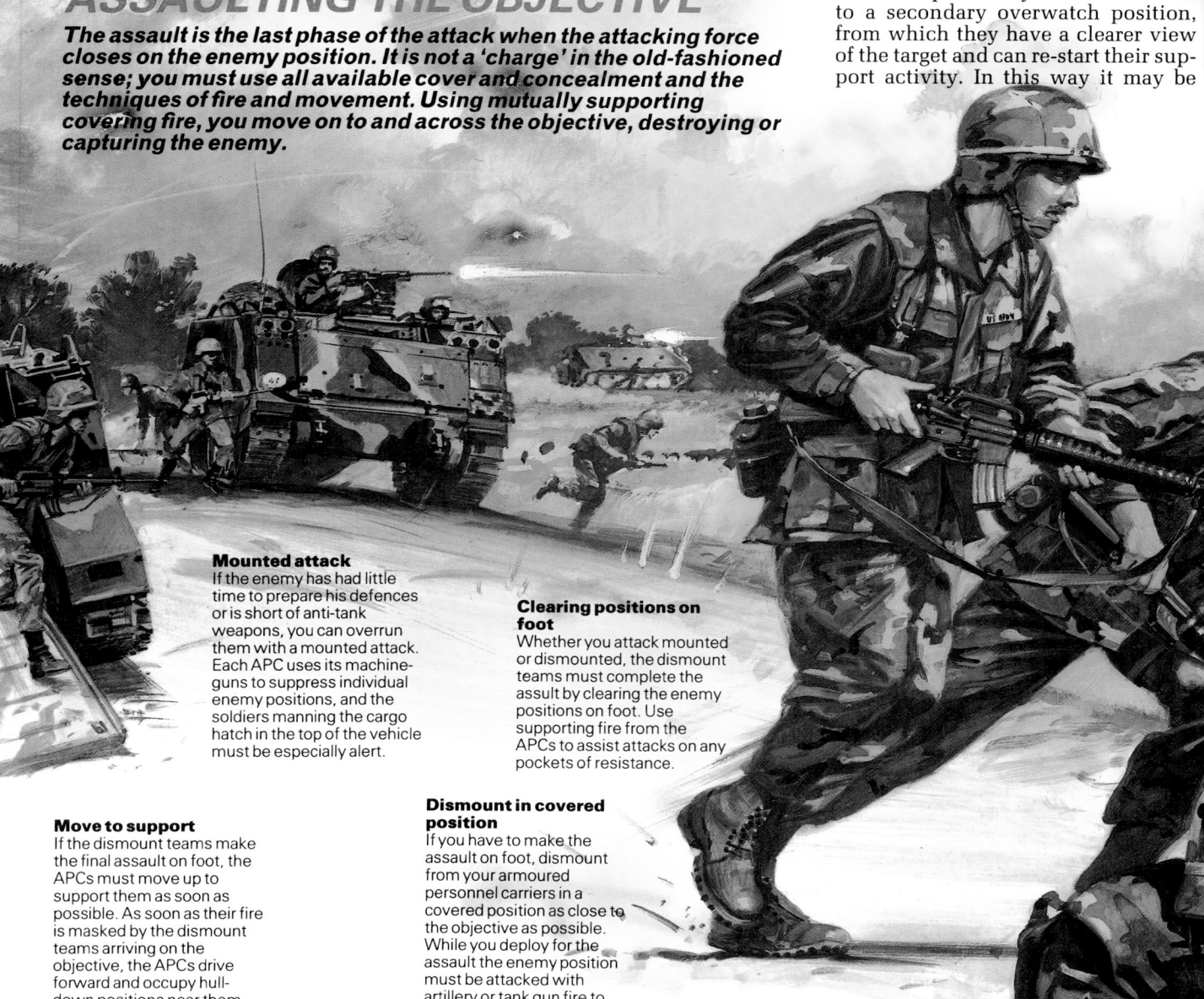

Mounted attack
If the enemy has had little time to prepare his defences or is short of anti-tank weapons, you can overrun them with a mounted attack. Each APC uses its machine-guns to suppress individual enemy positions, and the soldiers manning the cargo hatch in the top of the vehicle must be especially alert.

Clearing positions on foot
Whether you attack mounted or dismounted, the dismount teams must complete the assult by clearing the enemy positions on foot. Use supporting fire from the APCs to assist attacks on any pockets of resistance.

Move to support
If the dismount teams make the final assault on foot, the APCs must move up to support them as soon as possible. As soon as their fire is masked by the dismount teams arriving on the objective, the APCs drive forward and occupy hull-down positions near them.

Dismount in covered position
If you have to make the assault on foot, dismount from your armoured personnel carriers in a covered position as close to the objective as possible. While you deploy for the assault the enemy position must be attacked with artillery or tank gun fire to keep enemy anti-tank gunners at the bottom of their trenches.

DODGING ENEMY ANTI-TANK MISSILES

1 Look out for the tell-tale flash as the enemy anti-tank guided missile operator launches his missile.

2 Immediately fire all your machine guns at the enemy gunner: if it does not hit him it will at least disturb his aim.

4 Head for the nearest cover: a hollow or ridge is ideal, but trees, bushes or even telegraph poles can obstruct the missile's flight.

3 Drive in an erratic zig-zag to make it hard for the enemy to keep you in his sights.

1 Anti-tank missile operators need to keep the crosshairs of their sight centred on your vehicle. You must do everything you can to put them off.

2 Obstacles like bushes and small trees may not actually detonate the missile but they can snag its control wires, causing it to miss.

3 If all else fails you can try a sudden turn to right or left in the last seconds of the missile's flight.

---

possible to hit the enemy defensive position from both sides at once.

As soon as enemy resistance has been suppressed, the assault force must consolidate and reorganize, either to continue the attack or to prepare to repel a counterattack. When the troops have remained mounted on the vehicles right through the attack, it's often possible to push on and make much more significant gains in the relatively soft and ill-defended rear echelons.

Rear gains

In fact, gains made in the rear, which will contain command posts and assembly areas, may be considerably more important than taking the front line defensive positions, especially from an intelligence point of view.

Even though the fighting may be over at this point, the operation isn't. The captured areas have to be scoured for hidden dangers, both human and in the form of mines and booby traps; defensive positions have to be prepared; essential troops lost in the action – TOW and GPMG crews, for example – have to be replaced; re-supply organized; casualties and prisoners evacuated; and a detailed report of the operation made to higher command.

And even when all these follow-up tasks have been completed, still there's no time to relax. There's never time to relax on the battlefield.

Signal progress
As the dismount teams arrive on the objective they must signal their progress so that supporting fire can be shifted ahead of them. It's a good idea to have a pre-arranged visual signal such as coloured smoke grenades in case radio communication is not available at the vital moment.

Leading by example
In the assault, dismount team leaders must lead by example because it is practically impossible to shout orders above the noise of battle. 'Follow me and do as I do' is the way to lead.

Accurate shooting
Everyone's shooting must be properly directed for maximum effect. Since the squad leader is at the centre of the dismount team he fires his rifle at the centre of each target. He can also get the squad grenadier to use his M203 grenade launcher to mark targets with a smoke grenade.

Unarmed Combat Course No. 18

FACING TWO ATTACKERS Part 1

Defeating kicks and wristholds

If you are attacked by more than one person your survival depends on your ability to react quickly to each threat. In these sequences the defender faces two attackers and must switch instantly from one defensive technique to another.

1 One attacker comes at you from the front and uses a snap kick; you block his ankle with a cross-arm parry.

2 By twisting his ankle sharply you floor the attacker.

3 The second attacker appears to your left so you finish off attacker no. 1 with a kick to the groin.

4 Attacker no. 2 tries to pull you away with a wristhold.

5 Free your arm using an assisted release, swinging your body away from the attacker.

6 Now swing sharply back and deliver an elbow smash to the second attacker's jaw.

Defeating single wristhold and double arm grab

1 Faced by two attackers, one grabs you by the wrist.

2 Free your arm by swinging it outwards against his thumb.

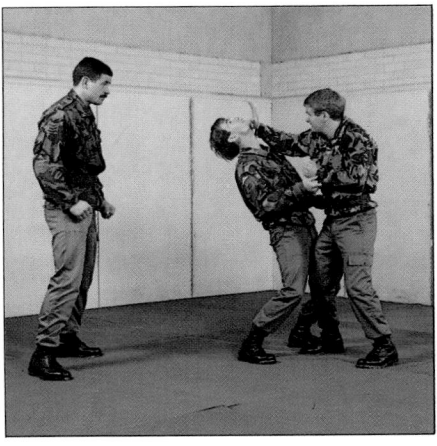

3 Follow up immediately by striking his chin with the palm of your hand.

4 Attacker no. 2 rushes forwards and tries to control you with a two-handed grab to your chest.

5 Counter this by grabbing his shoulders and pushing forward ready for a stomach throw.

6 Now pull his shoulders back, put your boot in his stomach and roll back, throwing the attacker upside down and onto the ground.

Unarmed Combat Course No. 19
DEFENCE AGAINST DOUBLE ARM HOLDS

In this sequence the defender is attacked from behind while he is dealing with a frontal assault. The key to success lies in reacting quickly as the situation changes, and remembering that just because the enemy to your front is down the fight may not yet be over.

1 The attacker comes at you from the front and attacks with a double arm hold.

2 You react by trapping the attacker's wrist.

3 Now deliver a sharp blow to the attacker's undefended throat. Do not use full force when practising this.

4 Having kept hold of his right arm, you can now apply an outside wristlock, forcing the attacker down.

5 As you twist his arm, attacker no. 1 is forced down but attacker no. 2 is closing in from behind. You quickly finish off the first attacker with a kick.

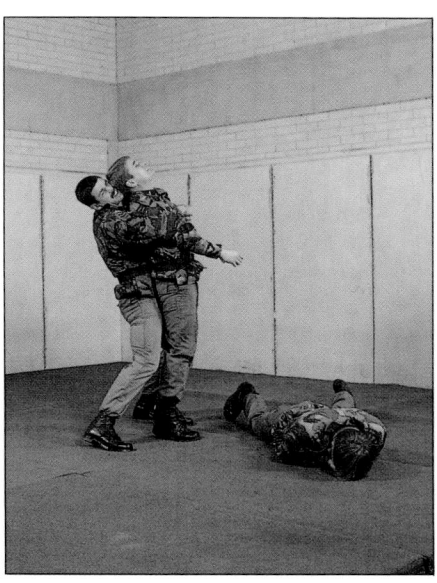

6 Just in time: the second attacker grabs you from behind, pinning your arms to your sides. To break free you bend down, which pulls him forward.

7 Snap your head backwards so that the back of your head butts him in the face.

8 While he is temporarily stunned you bend forward a second time, reaching for one of his ankles.

9 Pull sharply on his ankle and he topples over, landing on his back. Try not to lose hold of his foot.

10 Finish off the second attacker with a stamp to the groin.

Unarmed Combat Course No. 20

DEFENCE AGAINST DOUBLE STRANGLE HOLDS

In these sequences you are attacked with a mixture of arm chokes and strangles; we show you how to defeat each in turn. The defence against a rear strangle shown in issue 10 is no use if you are confronted by a second attacker, so in this sequence attacker no. 1 has to be finished off rather than left in a bent armlock.

Single arm choke & double hand strangle

1 You are attacked from behind without warning and the attacker applies a single arm choke.

2 Grab his wrist with your left hand and force his arm over your head, as shown in issue 10.

3 With a second attacker on the scene you must finish off attacker no. 1 quickly with a knee to the groin.

4 Attacker no. 2 comes into action and tries a double-handed strangle. You must respond quickly.

5 Drive your hands up between his arms and link your hands together.

6 Smash your hands down against the bridge of his nose.

Straight arm choke and strangle from the rear

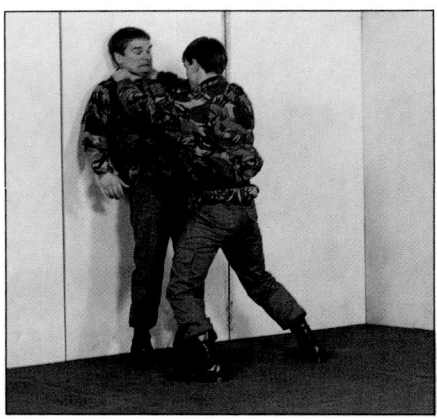

1 You are pinned to a wall by an attacker who is using a straight arm choke against you.

2 Bring your right hand over to grasp the attacker's right hand.

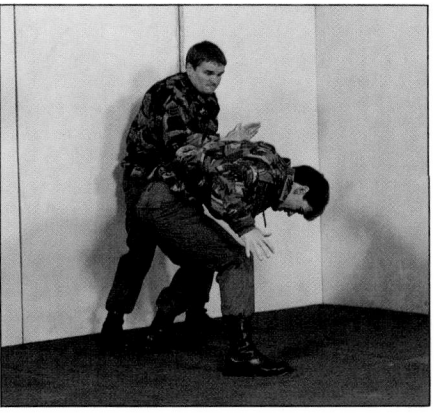

3 Rotate his arm to apply a wristlock, as shown in issue 9.

4 As in the previous move, you must finish off the first attacker when a second enemy appears on the scene.

5 A boot in the face and a savage twist of the arm finishes off attacker no. 1, but attacker no. 2 closes in.

6 Attacker no. 2 attacks you from behind and attempts to strangle you. You grab his neck with your right hand.

7 Throw him to the ground using a shoulder throw: get your hips under his centre of gravity and thrust upwards to topple the attacker over.

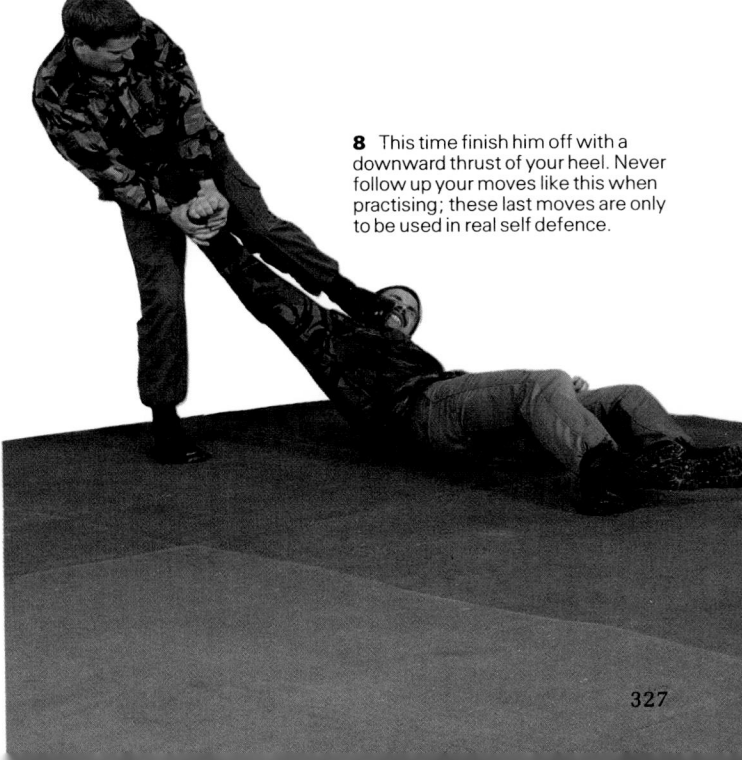

8 This time finish him off with a downward thrust of your heel. Never follow up your moves like this when practising; these last moves are only to be used in real self defence.

Lynx/TOW Tank-killer

An enemy armoured column suddenly changes the direction of its thrust, and tears through a weak section of the front. MILAN teams on the spot are overrun, and there's not enough time to deploy fresh units. But the Allied commander does have an ace up his sleeve – tank-killing Lynx helicopters, each armed with eight deadly Hughes TOW missiles.

Originally designed as a 12-seat light transport helicopter, the Lynx has been developed into one of the world's finest anti-armour missile platforms. The beautifully streamlined and lightweight fuselage and powerful Rolls-Royce Gem turboshaft engines make the Lynx one of the fastest helicopters over the battlefield – or anywhere. On 11 August 1986,

the modified Lynx demonstrator set a new helicopter absolute speed record of 216.45 knots, although standard Army Lynxes usually cruise at 120 knots.

The killer elite

The Lynx combines its high speed with superb manoeuvrability, so that it can fly swiftly to the battle area while twisting and turning at ultra-low level to make maximum use of cover. Helicopter pilots call this flying 'nap of earth': their aim is always to be behind or in front of high ground or trees, not outlined against the sky. Two further elements go to making Lynx such a formidable anti-tank weapon: its tremendous firepower and the men who fly it.

The Lynx AH.Mk 1 is armed with

eight Hughes BGM-71 TOW (Tube-launched, Optically-tracked, Wire-guided) anti-tank missiles, carried in groups of four launch tubes on each side of the fuselage. The missiles are powered by a two-stage (booster plus sustainer) rocket motor and have a maximum range of 3.75 kilometres, well beyond the range of most tank guns. After firing its missiles Lynx can be quickly re-armed, and spare TOW rounds can even be carried in the cabin. The use of a roof-mounted sight allows the pilot to keep the bulk of the aircraft low down behind cover while the gunner pinpoints the enemy. The sight currently fitted to the Lynx is not

This Lynx belongs to the Army Air Corps. The helicopter can operate independently, or in conjunction with other Army units or close-support aircraft.

This Lynx is firing a TOW missile. 'TOW' stands for Tube-launched, Optically-tracked, Wire-guided, but it spells trouble for any Soviet tank commander.

night or all-weather capable, but is being upgraded.

The Lynx is operated by a two-man crew, consisting of a pilot/aircraft commander in the right-hand seat and an aircrewman/gunner in the left hand seat. Most Army Air Corps air-crew are not commissioned, and the university-educated intellectual common in other areas of military aviation is something of a rarity in the Lynx force. These pilots and gunners tend to come from ordinary backgrounds, and are transformed into an elite fighting force by flair, dedication, esprit de corps, and a training that is second to none.

Tactics on the battlefield

The current philosophy is to use large numbers of helicopters as a Helarm (Helicopter armed action) to make a decisive attack on a division-

Tankbusting or trooping?

CREW

PERSONNEL

WEAPONS SYSTEM

The Lynx is used either as a missile-firing platform or in various load-carrying roles. The drawing above shows its configurations for the two missions.

sized enemy formation, gathering from previously surveyed ambush sites, known as Fire Positions, on pre-selected killing grounds. The Lynxes would usually be used as a commander's reserve, winning time for ground forces to redeploy or react in the face of an enemy thrust.

The key to success lies in the fact that the Lynx commander fights on ground of his own choosing, with good concealment, withdrawal routes and fields of fire. The tactics are to hit and run, falling back to other familiar fire positions to hit the enemy again. The Lynx can engage vastly more

Lynx 'Helarm'

The Helarm (Helicopter armed action) is probably the single most effective method of halting an enemy armoured thrust. But how does the Lynx find its target and move into the firing position? A typical action might take place in West Germany.

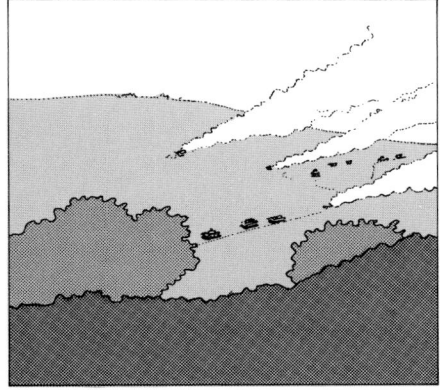

1 West Germany is superb anti-tank helicopter country, full of geographical features that channel enemy armour into predictable areas and easily-blockable 'choke points'.

2 If an enemy armoured division breaks through it will be found and kept under observation by a low-flying pair of Gazelle observation and reconnaissance helicopters.

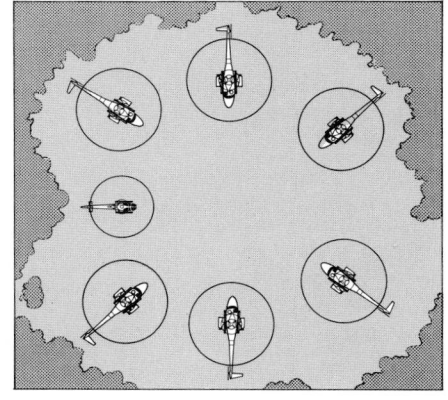

3 The Lynxes wait to be called forward at the 'holding RV', arranged in a circle to allow a good look-out to be maintained, with each Lynx covering the rear of the opposite aircraft.

Inside the Lynx

In any future conflict, the threat of NBC (Nuclear, Biological and Chemical) contamination would be severe; crew and passengers would routinely wear heavy and uncomfortable NBC protective clothing. The cabin is large and spacious, with canvas bench seats to accommodate up to nine soldiers. Troops would not usually be carried on a mission in which TOW missiles were used.

Aircrewman/gunner
The left-hand seat is occupied by the aircrewman, who acts as the gunner and assists the pilot with navigation and communications.

Pilot
The right-hand seat is occupied by the pilot/aircraft commander, whose hands are full just flying the Lynx!

Warhead
The Hughes TOW contains a shaped-charge HEAT (High Explosive Anti-Tank) warhead, capable of penetrating the thickest armour.

Control fins
Tail-mounted control fins and stabilising fins mounted amidships flick out as soon as the missile leaves its tube.

numerous enemy armoured forces with direct fire or by inserting anti-tank missile teams, and can act independently as well as in concert with armour, infantry, artillery or close air support.

Guidance wires
Twin guidance wires transmit flightpath corrections to the missile from the gunner's joystick, via the SACLOS (Semi-Automatic Command to Line Of Sight) system.

Request for action

A request for a Lynx Helarm can come directly from a ground unit, or more usually from an obs and recce (observation and reconnaissance) pair of Gazelles. These two helicopters fly nap of earth, looking for and keeping track of the enemy while staying just out of range of his MBT (Main Battle Tank) armament, anti-aircraft artillery and small arms fire. They report back to the Helarm commander in the lead Lynx, and to the Helarm director in a third Gazelle.

During hostilities, a Lynx squadron would operate from a temporary HLS (Helicopter Landing Site), which would itself move as often as twice a day. Sometimes an HLS would be set up in woodland: support vehicles and tents will hide in the trees, and the

helicopters will park on the edge of an adjacent field, covered by camouflage netting. More often, an urban site would be used, with the helicopters parked in a supermarket or filling station, since buildings give better concealment and protection against NBC (nuclear, biological, chemical) weapons and blast. All personnel would work in full NBC protective clothing, and would rest in a 'Porton liner', an inflatable tent with 'clean' air and a system of air-locks, or in a

vehicle-mounted 'protection unit', based on a four-ton box body.

Out of hiding...

When action is imminent, the Lynx squadron goes to 15 minutes standby. While the pilots take the camouflage off their aircraft, or get them into the open, the crewmen are briefed in the Squadron Command Post (CP). The aircraft then fly to the 'holding RV' (holding rendezvous), a safe field or clearing within a few minutes' flight

4 Messages are passed on using small code cards which are read through the TOW sight, or by flashing the landing lights. Radio conversation, where necessary, is usually in code.

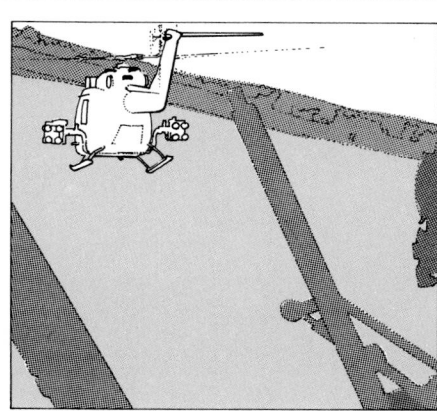

5 The group splits into two three-aircraft fire-teams and these fly 'nap of earth' to the fire position, keeping as low as possible to take full advantage of terrain masking.

6 The ideal fire position provides a screen of cover in front of the aircraft. From the front only the rotors and roof mounted sight should be visible, except when the Lynx pops up to fire.

Rotor
The Lynx's semi-rigid titanium rotor head is uniquely strong and flexible, and allows unparalleled manoeuvrability.

Cabin
The Lynx can accommodate nine fully-armed troops in its capacious cabin, with two crew members in the cockpit.

Engines
The Lynx is powered by two Rolls-Royce Gem turboshaft engines, mounted side-by-side on top of the upper fuselage decking.

TOW tubes
The Lynx AH.Mk 1 carries four TOW missile launch tubes on each side of the fuselage. Reloads can be carried in the cabin, but this is not usual.

of the selected fire position. The aircraft wait, sometimes with one engine shut down to conserve fuel, until called forward by the Helarm director in a Gazelle. The Lynxes sit in a wide circle, pointing inwards to allow code-cards held up by the Helarm commander to be read by the other crewmen through their TOW sights. This arrangement also allows a full 360° lookout against enemy aircraft or troops, with each crew looking

beyond the helicopter opposite them in the circle.

Flying from the holding RV to a final RV or directly to the fire position, the pilot makes the maximum use of cover, sacrificing speed for an unseen approach, hover-taxiing very low, often into a fire position familiar from peacetime exercises. Sometimes a fire position will be in front of a line of trees, against which the black and green Lynx will hardly be visible or,

more often, behind trees or a ridge. If behind cover the Lynx will expose only its rotors and roof-mounted sight for the aircrewman to get on a target, popping up briefly to fire, and then slipping back.

. . . into the firing line

The squadron's six Lynxes would usually have split into two fire teams of three at the final RV, either going forward to two separate fire positions, or using the same fire position in a

7 The gunner of the Lynx selects a target from the sector assigned to his helicopter, and uses a small joystick to position the sight cross-hairs over it.

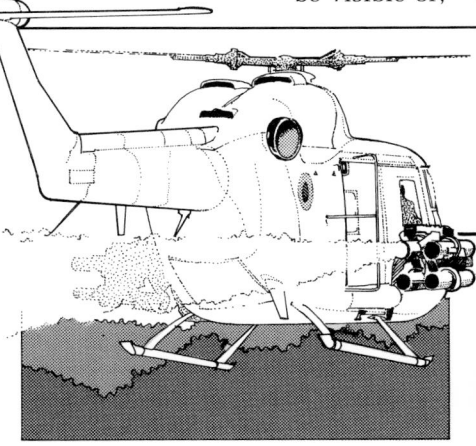

8 The gunner grasps the trigger in his right hand and the joystick in his right hand. He has already selected which TOW he wishes to fire, and does so when the Lynx pops up above its cover.

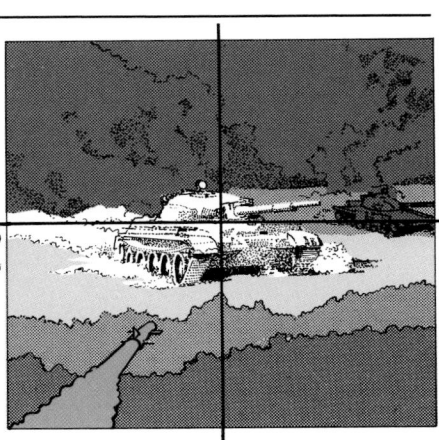

9 The sight of the TOW missile automatically tracks the weapon, and steers it to the target centred in the cross-hairs.

331

relay. The leader of each fire team usually flies the middle aircraft at the fire position, and is responsible for destroying close and mid-range targets, in that order. The outer aircraft concentrates on the flanks, on extreme-range targets. When all missiles have been fired, or if forced back by enemy fire, the fire team would withdraw to the flank.

When operating with fixed-wing support aircraft against an enemy

No. 3 Commando Brigade Air Squadron, operators of this Lynx, is frequently deployed to Norway where its aircraft usually receive a temporary, but highly effective, winter camouflage.

Battlefield Evaluation: comparing

Westland Lynx AH.Mk 1 and AH.Mk 7

Specification:
Length overall: 15.163 m
Rotor diameter: 12.80 m
Maximum cruising speed: 140 knots
Range: 540 km
Standard weapon load: eight Hughes TOW missiles

The British Army is the only military user of the Army Lynx. Originally ordered purely as a utility transport helicopter, the Lynx nevertheless performs creditably in the Helarm role, although concern has been voiced about its fragility. The Lynx has almost completely replaced the older, but more robust, Westland Scout. The AH.Mk 7 has slightly uprated engines and a new tail rotor.

Assessment
Manoeuvrability ★★★★★
All weather capability ★
Versatility ★★★★★
Worldwide users ★

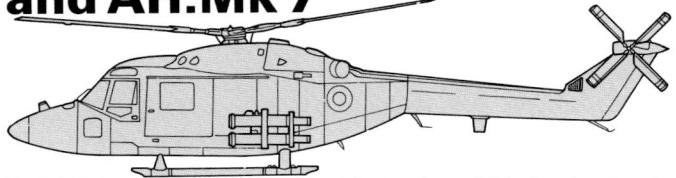

British Army Lynxes are armed with eight Hughes TOW missiles, but have been tested with other weapons.

Mil Mi-24 'Hind-D'

Specification:
Length overall: 21.50 m
Rotor diameter: 17.0 m
Maximum cruising speed: 159 knots
Range: 750 km
Standard weapon load: four UV-32-57 rocket pods; four AT-2 'Sagger' missiles; one four-barrel 12.7-mm cannon

The 'Hind' is fast, heavily-armed and well-protected. The four-man cockpit of early variants has been replaced by a tandem two-seat gunship nose, usually incorporating a four-barrel 12.7-mm cannon turret. 'Hind-F', however, has two fixed 23-mm guns on the starboard cabin side. All variants can carry up to four UV-32-57 rocket pods, each containing 32 57-mm rockets, and four AT-2 'Swatter' or AT-6 'Spiral' anti-tank missiles.

Assessment
Manoeuvrability ★
All weather capability ★
Versatility ★★★
Worldwide users ★★★★★

Despites its armour, 'Hind' has proved rather vulnerable to ground fire in Afghanistan and Angola.

Hughes AH-64 Apache

Specification:
Length overall: 17.76 m
Rotor diameter: 14.63 m
Maximum cruising speed: 155 knots
Range: 482 km
Standard weapon load: M230 30-mm Chain Gun'; 16 Hellfire anti-tank missiles

The AH-64 is packed with sophisticated avionics and systems, which allow real night/all-weather operation. It is also heavily armed and well armoured. Although extremely capable, the AH-64 is also very vulnerable, having to pop up to acquire, fire and track its weapons; a roof- or mast-mounted sight would allow the gunner to observe a target from behind cover. The Apache has proved troublesome in service, with numerous groundings of the whole fleet.

Assessment
Manoeuvrability ★★★
All weather capability ★★★★★
Versatility ★★
Worldwide users ★

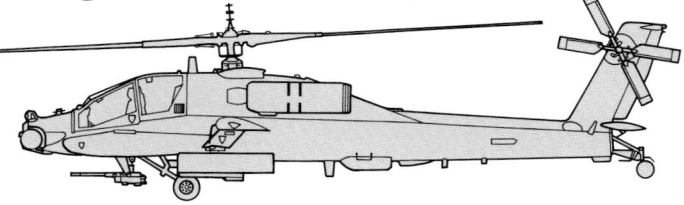

The AH-64 is enormously capable, but many believe it would prove too complicated to maintain during any war.

column, the Lynx would concentrate on enemy anti-aircraft artillery vehicles, leaving the tanks to USAF A-10 Thunderbolts or RAF Harriers.

It seems likely that the Army Air Corps will receive the much-improved Lynx-3 as its new anti-tank helicopter. The aircraft, armed with fire-and-forget Rockwell Hellfire missiles, will give new capabilities for long-range engagements, but that's another story.

The British Army now seems certain to replace its Lynxes in the anti-tank role with the Lynx-3. This has cannon fitted on pylons outside the aircraft, and can carry Hellfire missiles.

the Lynx with its rivals

Bell 209 AH-1 HueyCobra

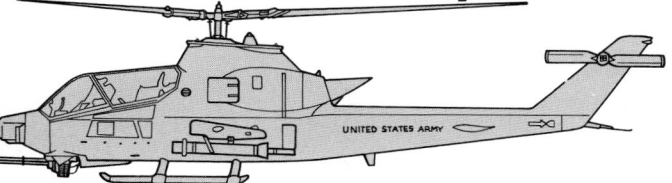

Basically a gunship version of the UH-1 Iroquois, with the same rotor, powerplant and transmission, the AH-1 introduced a new slender fuselage, with tandem seating for a gunner and pilot. The basic aircraft has been progressively developed to take advantage of new weapons and fire control systems. The AH-1 has been used in action in Vietnam and Grenada by the US, by the Israelis in various conflicts and by Iran in the Gulf War.

Specification:
Length overall: 16.18 m
Rotor diameter: 13.41 m
Maximum cruising speed: 122 knots
Range: 407 km
Standard weapon load: eight TOW missiles; one 20-mm or 30-mm cannon in nose turret; two 2.75-in rocket pods

Assessment
Manoeuvrability ★★★
All weather capability ★
Versatility ★
Worldwide users ★★★★

The AH-1 HueyCobra is the world's best-known attack helicopter, and has an impressive combat record.

Messerschmitt-Bölkow-Blohm BO 105

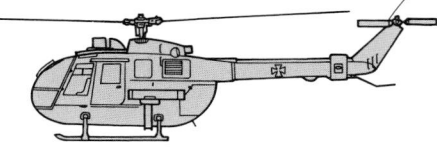

The BO 105 is small, fast, and highly manoeuvrable, and armed versions have been widely exported. Sweden has TOW-equipped aircraft, while Spain and Germany use HOT missiles. Spain also operates some 20-mm cannon-armed aircraft in the escort role. Trials have been undertaken with mast-mounted and helmet-mounted sights, and with advanced electro-optical sensor systems.

Specification:
Length overall: 11.86 m
Rotor diameter: 9.84 m
Maximum cruising speed: 131 knots
Range: 575 km
Standard weapon load: six Euromissile HOT missiles

Assessment
Manoeuvrability ★★★★★
All weather capability ★★
Versatility ★★★★
Worldwide users ★★★

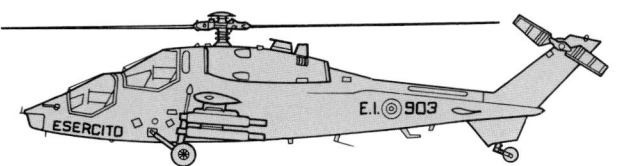

The BO 105P PAH-1 forms the backbone of Germany's anti-tank helicopter strength.

Agusta A 129 Mangusta

The Mangusta uses the same Rolls-Royce Gem turboshafts as the Lynx, but has a dedicated gunship-type fuselage with pilot and gunner in tandem seats. The aircraft is equipped with sophisticated navigation, weapons-aiming and flight control systems, and there is provision for a mast-mounted sight. The aircraft is heavily armoured, yet remains commendably swift and agile.

Specification:
Length overall: 14.29 m
Rotor diameter: 11.90 m
Maximum cruising speed: 130 knots
Range: not released
Standard weapon load: eight TOW missiles; two rocket or 20-mm gun pods

Assessment
Manoeuvrability ★★★
All weather capability ★★★★
Versatility ★★
Worldwide users ★

The Agusta 129 Mangusta is Europe's answer to the AH-64 – slightly less sophisticated, but very much cheaper.

Weapons and Equipment Guide No. 16

Leopard in the Front Line

The monstrous Rheinmetall 120-mm guns carried by the Leopard 2s are over five metres long. They fire armour-piercing shell to an effective range of 3,500 metres at a velocity more than five times the speed of sound.

In World War II the main strength of the German army fought against the Russians and was defeated in a series of massive armoured battles in Eastern Europe. In many cases the German tanks were superior to the crude fighting vehicles of the Red Army, but the cheaper and simpler Soviet tanks smashed their way right into Berlin.

Today the West German army is equipped with 1,800 Leopard 2s, some of the finest tanks in the world, but the Soviets still have the numbers on their side. No-one knows for certain whether modern Western technology can bridge the gap.

The Leopard 2 is a third-generation Main Battle Tank incorporating the very latest in weapons technology. Protected by advanced armour which can defeat the warheads of most infantry anti-tank weapons and fitted with a new powerplant and suspension system, the Leopard 2 is tougher and more mobile on the battlefield than any of its predecessors. Extensive use of computers and automated equipment enable the Leopard to hit first, hit hard and keep on hitting with its 120-mm smoothbore gun.

The earlier models of the Leopard are armed with a 105-mm gun, but Rheinmetall calculated that only a

The Leopard 2 is exceptionally well protected by advanced armour that is designed to withstand attack by the shaped warheads fitted to infantry ATGMs.

120-mm weapon would be able to defeat the frontal armour of the latest generation of Soviet tanks. The Leopard 2's 120-mm gun fires APFSDS-T (Armour Piercing Fin Stabilized Discarding Sabot Tracer): the

shell is fired at very high velocity, 1,650 metres per second, and contains a very dense core of tungsten alloy. By striking the target with such ferocity the core can penetrate the heaviest tank armour.

The specialized anti-tank rounds have only limited effectiveness against infantry and in particular the tank crew's great enemy, the anti-tank guided missile. The Leopard's secondary ammunition is a HEAT round which is dual purpose; it relies on the chemical energy of its explosion to burn a hole through armour plate, and its fragmentation effect gives it more value against infantry targets than APFSDS. Unfortunately, though, its lower velocity and high trajectory make it less accurate.

Smoothbore gun

The Leopard 2 is the first Western tank to have a smoothbore gun, 20 years after the Soviets pioneered the use of smoothbore tank armament with the U-5TS 115-mm gun carried by the T-62. Where a rifled gun imparts a spin to the shell, which stabilizes its flight, the shells from a smoothbore need to have fins that pop out after they leave the barrel.

The Soviets encountered some difficulties with their first smoothbore: at long ranges a crosswind would alter the course of a shell as the fins acted like a weather vane and turned the shell into the wind. But they firmly believe that most tank gunnery takes place at under 2,000 metres, where this is not a severe drawback.

The British 120-mm rifled gun, carried by Chieftain and Challenger

The turret front and sides are defended by thick slabs of advanced armour, and the hull front is very well sloped to provide maximum protection. The bulbous lump in the gun barrel is a glass-reinforced plastic fume extractor.

Despite being much heavier than the Leopard 1, the Leopard 2 is actually more mobile on rough ground, thanks to its incredibly powerful engine.

The Leopard 2 is able to climb a 60 per cent gradient and cope with a 30 per cent side slope, and it can tackle a vertical obstacle up to 1.1 metres high.

tanks, theoretically has a better performance at very long range, but after testing the British and German 120-mm guns the US Army selected the German weapon for the M1A1. The Rheinmetall gun has a theoretical barrel life of over 1,000 rounds and is chromium-plated to cope with the immense strain of firing large projectiles at four times the speed of sound. Recent tests have shown that accuracy begins to deteriorate after the first 400 shots.

The Arab-Israeli tank battles of

The main armament is fully stabilised and keeps the gun on target while the Leopard crashes across rough ground. The computer system that directs the Leopard's gunnery takes into account the relative movement of the Leopard and its target as well as the range, wind direction and type of ammunition.

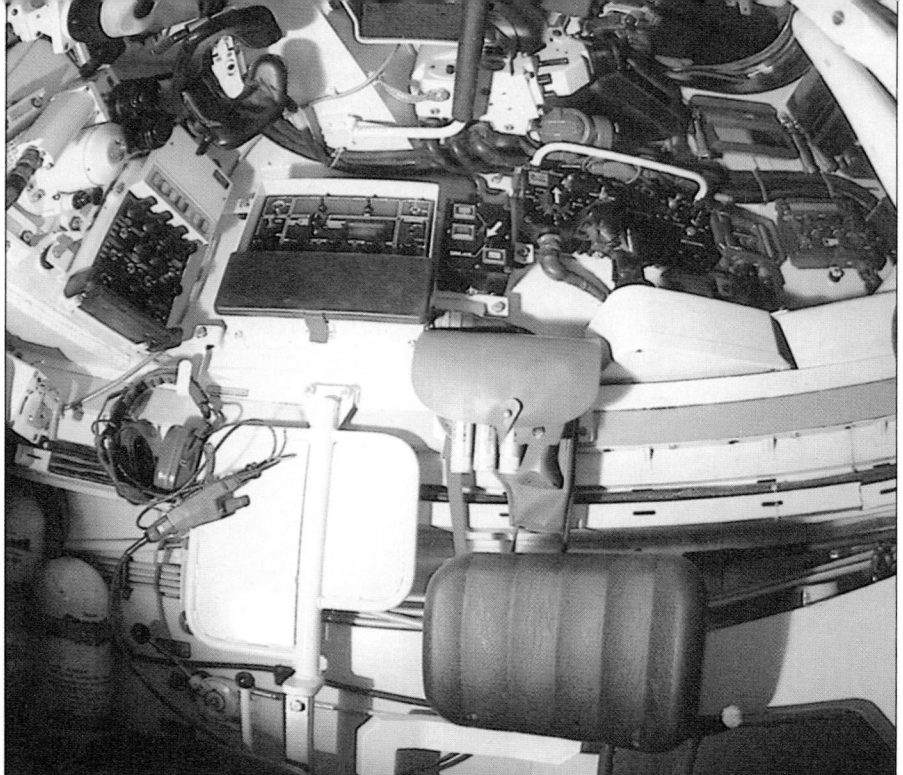

Inside the Leopard

Driver
The driver enters and e the vehicle via a single-piece hatch cover whic opens to the right. Whe the hatch is closed he re on three periscopes, th centre one of which ca replaced by a passive n periscope.

120-mm Rheinmetall smoothbore gun
Fires either armour-piercing or dual-purpose anti-armour/anti-personnel ammunition, which is fin-stabilized for accuracy. The cartridge cases are semi-combustible and the metal base of each round drops into a bag underneath the gun after firing.

Advanced armour
The Leopard's front hull and turret are protected by advanced armour, the details of which are classified. This is proof against the HEAT warheads of most infantry anti-tank weapons.

Ammunition in hull
The bulk of the Leopard's 42 rounds are stored in the hull, where they are protected by the very thick frontal armour.

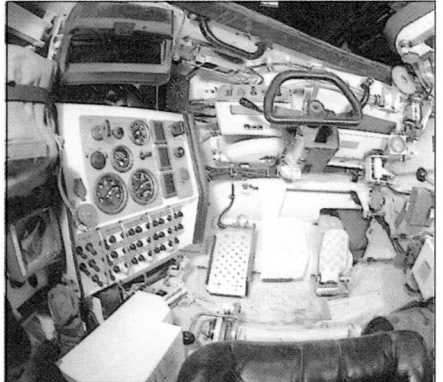

The driver's station: the automatic transmission and variable steering make the Leopard 2 less tiring to drive than any other tank.

Inside the Leopard's large turret you can see the loader's seat on the left-hand side. Having this fourth crewman is better than using an auto-loader.

1967-73 demonstrated the importance of mobility: a tank must be able to travel cross-country at a fair speed, to accelerate away from a firing position quickly and to have a long range. The Leopard 2 is one of the fastest Main Battle Tanks in the world, with a top road speed of over 70 km/h; the only rivals are the M1 Abrams and the T-72/80.

Battlefield mobility

On rough ground the Leopard is surprisingly mobile, throwing its great weight across the battlefield with the agility of an armoured personnel carrier thanks to its turbocharged 12-cylinder diesel engine. This gives the Leopard a power-to-weight ratio equalled only by the Abrams.

It is all very well for an armoured

vehicle to crash across the countryside at high speed, but if the journey is too exhausting for the crew members then the tank will not put up a good performance when it meets any opposition. Driver fatigue has been a problem for armoured forces since tanks were invented, but the Leopard 2 has an advanced automatic transmission that saves the driver from having to fight with a clutch pedal throughout the journey.

Driver fatigue

The double clutching required on the earlier T-54/55 and T-62 Soviet tanks was a source of endless trouble, particularly in the Middle East, where the heat and effort of more than half an hour's driving seriously affected the driver's performance. By contrast, the Leopard's transmission and suspension allow it to travel cross-country faster than most crews can react.

The fire control computer receives the range of the target from the range-finder and guides the main armament to the line of sight of the gunner's periscope. It aims the gun to allow for the tilt of the vehicle; the relative speeds and direction of the Leopard and of the target; any crosswind that might affect the path of the shell; and the flight characteristics of the type of ammunition being fired. The system allows the Leopard to shoot with considerable accuracy even while moving cross-country.

Under their armoured skins tanks contain an alarming mixture of inflammable fuel and high explosive ammunition: if an enemy shell should punch through the armour the crew are often doomed to burn to death where they sit. Like the M1 Abrams, the Leopard protects the crew from an ammunition explosion by having 'blow off' panels positioned above the shells stored in the turret rear. A hit on this area simply blows away the panels and the force of the explosion passes upwards while the crew are the other side of armoured doors. The rest of the ammunition is stored in the hull, which is far less vulnerable to enemy fire.

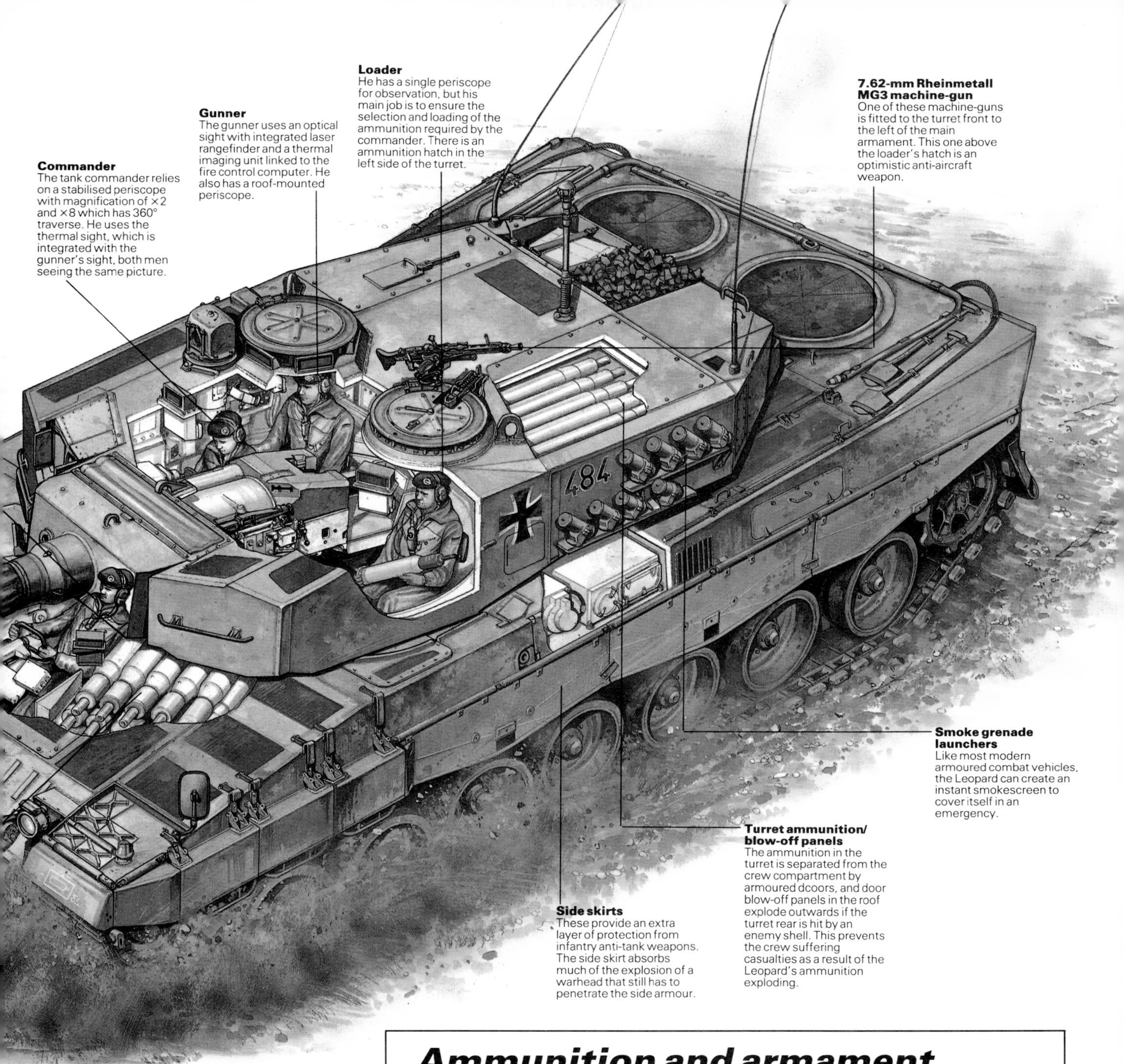

Commander
The tank commander relies on a stabilised periscope with magnification of ×2 and ×8 which has 360° traverse. He uses the thermal sight, which is integrated with the gunner's sight, both men seeing the same picture.

Gunner
The gunner uses an optical sight with integrated laser rangefinder and a thermal imaging unit linked to the fire control computer. He also has a roof-mounted periscope.

Loader
He has a single periscope for observation, but his main job is to ensure the selection and loading of the ammunition required by the commander. There is an ammunition hatch in the left side of the turret.

7.62-mm Rheinmetall MG3 machine-gun
One of these machine-guns is fitted to the turret front to the left of the main armament. This one above the loader's hatch is an optimistic anti-aircraft weapon.

Smoke grenade launchers
Like most modern armoured combat vehicles, the Leopard can create an instant smokescreen to cover itself in an emergency.

Turret ammunition/blow-off panels
The ammunition in the turret is separated from the crew compartment by armoured doors, and door blow-off panels in the roof explode outwards if the turret rear is hit by an enemy shell. This prevents the crew suffering casualties as a result of the Leopard's ammunition exploding.

Side skirts
These provide an extra layer of protection from infantry anti-tank weapons. The side skirt absorbs much of the explosion of a warhead that still has to penetrate the side armour.

To protect the crew against the ghastly consequences of a penetrative hit through the hull, the Leopard 2 is fitted with an inert gas fire suppression system designed to put out a fire in one-fifth of a second. Otherwise a penetration of the fuel tanks by a shaped charge warhead can result in a fatal mixture of fuel, air and heat.

Front-line service

The Leopard 2, the British Challenger and the M1 Abrams represent the latest and greatest in Western tank design. They are expected to serve in the front line for at least the next 10 and probably the next 20 years. Further improvements in fire control systems

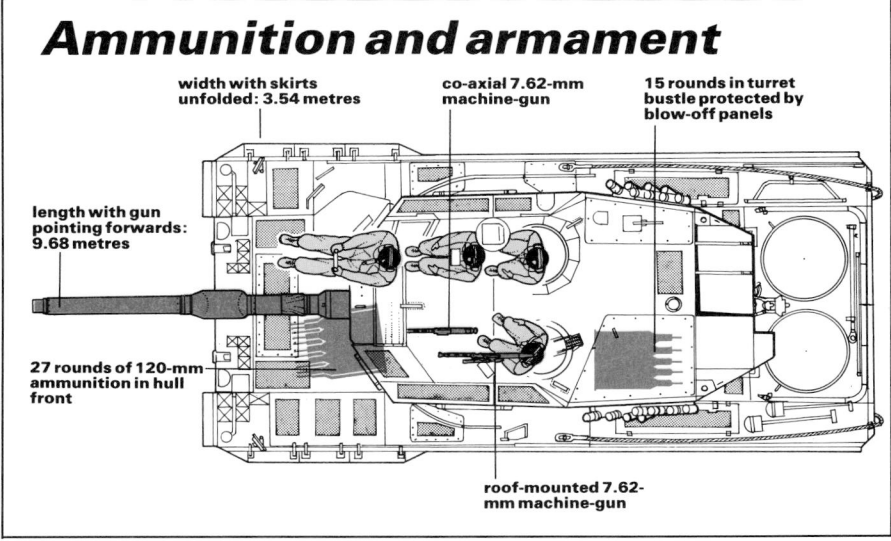

Ammunition and armament

width with skirts unfolded: 3.54 metres

co-axial 7.62-mm machine-gun

15 rounds in turret bustle protected by blow-off panels

length with gun pointing forwards: 9.68 metres

27 rounds of 120-mm ammunition in hull front

roof-mounted 7.62-mm machine-gun

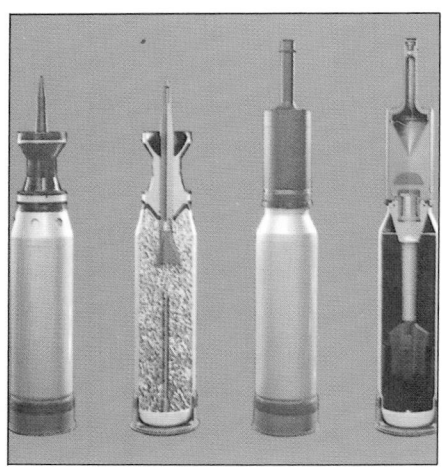

and automation can be expected, but the overall 'classic' layout of the tank is unlikely to be done away with in the immediate future.

New ammunition is continually being developed, and as every effort is made to improve the performance of the older 105-mm guns in NATO tanks further improvements to the newer 120-mm weapons will follow. One possibility for the future is an anti-helicopter round: at the moment neither the hyper-velocity tungsten-cored anti-tank ammunition nor the

The Leopard's ammunition sectioned: on the left is the APDSFS round with its dense penetrating core, and, on the right, the multi-purpose HEAT round.

dual purpose HEAT shells are of much value against enemy helicopters, which now pose a serious threat to MBTs.

Helicopter threat

Prototype Leopard 2s were tested with a 20-mm cannon in the commander's position on the turret roof, but this calibre is unsatisfactory for engaging helicopters equipped with missiles effective at 3,000 metres. Perhaps the answer will be a new type of shell fired from the main armament.

The total production run of Leopard 2s will be less than 3,000 tanks. This compares to nearly 9,000 T-72s, over 9,000 T-64s and approaching 1,500

Battlefield Evaluation: comparing

Leopard 2

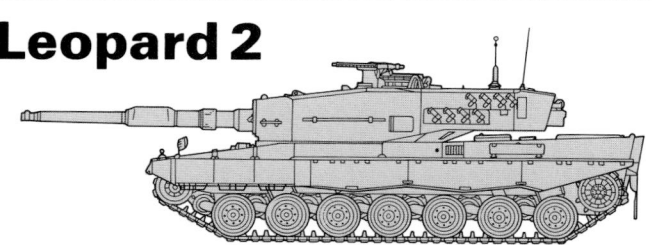

Equipped with the most sophisticated and probably the most expensive fire control system of any main Battle Tank, the Leopard 2 has few equals. Only the M1 Abrams has comparable equipment and these two tanks represent the 'top of the market' in Western armour. The Leopard 2 has exceptional battlefield mobility, long range and massive firepower, but whether its superiority to modern Soviet tanks is enough to match their vastly superior numbers is an uncomfortable question.

Specification:
Combat weight: 55 tonnes
Road speed: 72 km/h
Power to weight ratio: 27 hp/tonne
Length: 7.72 m
Height: 2.48 m
Crew: 4
Armament: 1×120-mm Rheinmetall smoothbore; 2×7.62-mm machine-guns

Assessment
Firepower ★★★★★
Protection ★★★★★
Age ★★★
Worldwide users ★★

With advanced armour and extensive computerization, the Leopard 2 is the last word in Western tank design.

M1 Abrams

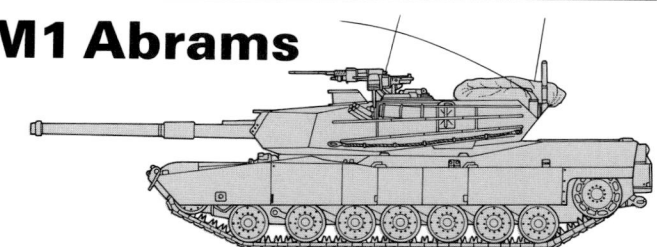

When developing the Leopard 2 the West Germans tested but ultimately rejected the gas turbine in favour of a conventional diesel engine. Its great rival, the M1 Abrams, encountered some difficulty with the turbine but the teething problems are over and it is proving very successful. The M1 has a fractionally higher power-to-weight ratio than the Leopard and carries the same armament. Both are literally million-dollar vehicles and NATO will depend heavily on them for the next 20 years.

Specification:
Combat weight: 54.5 tonnes
Road speed: 72 km/h
Power to weight ratio: 27 hp/tonne
Length: 7.9 m
Height: 2.3 m
Crew: 4
Armament: 1×120-mm Rheinmetall smoothbore; 1×0.50-cal; 1×7.62-mm machine-gun

Assessment
Firepower ★★★★★
Protection ★★★★★
Age ★★★
Worldwide users ★

The M1 Abrams is broadly equal to the Leopard 2, but doubts remain about its gas turbine engine.

T-72

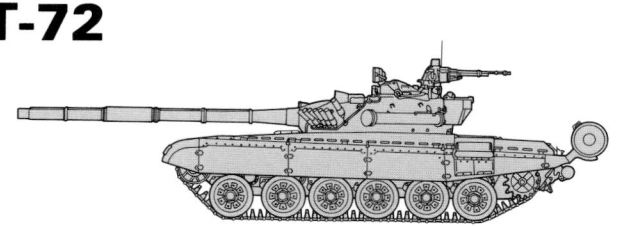

For the last 30 years NATO has drawn some comfort from the thought that Soviet tanks are inferior to those of Western armies, and so their numerical superiority is not quite the advantage it seems. However, the latest generation of Soviet armour has narrowed the technology gap and is being churned out in traditionally vast numbers. With its simple transmission, unpadded tracks and massive production run the T-72 is far cheaper than the Leopard 2, even if it is individually inferior.

Specification:
Combat weight: 41 tonnes
Road speed: 60 km/h
Power to weight ratio: 19 hp/tonne
Length: 6.95 m
Height: 2.37 m
Crew: 3
Armament: 1×125-mm smoothbore; 1×12.7-mm and 1×7.62-mm machine-guns

Assessment
Firepower ★★★★★
Protection ★★★
Age ★★★
Worldwide users ★★★

Light but heavily-armed, the T-72 is in widespread service with the Warsaw Pact armies.

T-80s already in service with Soviet forces. As a whole, Warsaw Pact tank forces outnumber those of NATO by nearly 3:1, and the Soviets have not allowed the increasing sophistication and cost of their latest tanks to reduce this advantage.

The Leopard 2 is a formidable combat vehicle, individually superior to any Soviet tank. Whether it is so superior that it can take on several times its own numbers will hopefully remain unanswered.

Eighteen hundred Leopard 2s will be serving in the West German army when production is completed this year, but NATO tank forces in Germany will still be heavily outnumbered.

the 'Leopard' with its rivals

T-62

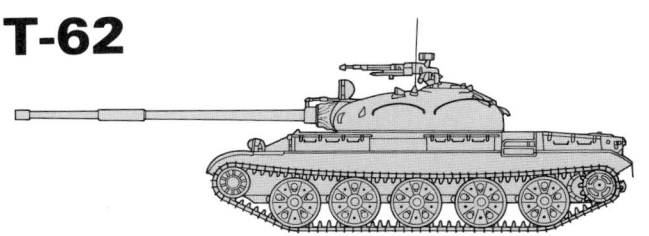

The T-62 belongs to the generation of tanks that includes the Chieftain, the Leopard 1 and the American M60. It entered production in 1961 and was the mainstay of the Syrian forces in the 1973 Arab-Israeli war. In the Middle East the poor quality of the Arab crews combined with the weaknesses of the T-62 to produce a tank force utterly inferior to the Israelis'. The T-62 soldiers on in the Warsaw Pact, and is in service in Afghanistan, although first-line Soviet units now use T-64/72/80 MBTs.

Specification:
Combat weight: 40 tonnes
Road speed: 50 km/h
Power to weight ratio: 14.5 hp/tonne
Length: 6.63 m
Height: 2.4 m
Crew: 4
Armament: 1×115-mm smoothbore; 1×12.7-mm and 1×7.62-mm machine-guns

Assessment
Firepower ★★★
Protection ★★★
Age ★★★★★
Worldwide users ★★★★★

Typical of the older style Soviet tanks, the T-62 is uncomfortable, but well-armed and mechanically sound.

Merkava

The Israeli Merkava incorporates all the lessons of 30 years of armoured warfare in the Middle East and, unlike both NATO and Soviet tanks, it gives first priority to protection rather than mobility or firepower. Also as a result of Israeli combat experience, the Merkava can carry almost twice as much ammuniton as NATO and Soviet MBTs: up to 85 105-mm shells. The latest Merkava will have a new power pack which will give it a much higher power to weight ratio, but in the meantime the Merkava remains a slow but very well protected heavy tank.

Specification:
Combat weight: 60 tonnes
Road speed: 46 km/h
Power to weight ratio: 15 hp/tonne
Length: 7.45 m
Height: 2.64 m
Crew: 4
Armament: 1×105-mm rifled gun; 3×7.62-mm amachine-guns; 1×0.50-cal machine-gun; 1×60-mm mortar

Assessment
Firepower ★★★★★
Protection ★★★★★
Age ★★
Worldwide users ★

Very heavily armoured and carrying a large shell supply, the Merkava is built for prolonged day/night combat.

EE-T1 Osorio

The increasing cost of the latest Western tanks has helped spur other nations into producing their own, the Brazilian Osorio tank is a particularly attractive option for a Third World nation. It uses as many existing components as possible and can be tailored to suit the particular requirements of a customer. The Brazilian army is expected to order some 500 tanks in the next few years, and Iraq, which is already using Brazilian weapons in the Gulf War, is also interested.

Specification:
Combat weight: 41 tonnes
Road speed: 70 km/h
Power to weight ratio: 25 hp/tonne
Length: 7.13 m
Height: 2.37 m
Crew: 4
Armament: 1×105-mm rifled or 120-mm smoothbore gun; 2×7.62-ma machine-guns

Assessment
Firepower ★★★★
Protection ★★★
Age ★
Worldwide users ★

Brazil's Osorio is a capable vehicle and far cheaper than the latest NATO tanks.

Colt .45
Combat
Classic

The Colt .45 M1911A1 Government Model: a very solid performer and the sidearm of the US Army from the trenches of World War I to the jungles of Vietnam. The massive .45 bullet is widely regarded as one of the few rounds with sufficient ballistic efficiency to sledge down a drug crazed criminal or terrorist without using expanding ammunition, and it significantly out-performs 9-mm Parabellum without suffering from the problems of over penetration.

For many years the US Army has been trying to adopt a new pistol to replace the Colt .45 automatic which entered service in 1911, but the popular reputation of this ancient weapon makes it an impossible task. The majority of the world's armies outside the Warsaw Pact adopted the 9-mm Parabellum cartridge long ago, but the .45 is considered to be as American as apple pie. The second problem is that in each of the prolonged competitions to find a successor, American weapons were among the first to be eliminated and, in a land devoted to the cult of the pistol, the idea of adopting a foreign weapon has gone down like a lead balloon.

The story behind the American love affair with the Colt .45 began with John Browning, who took out a number of patents covering possible methods of operating automatic pistols in 1897. Within a year he and the Colt company to whom he had licensed all the patents were demonstrating a .38 calibre automatic to the US Army. The Army tested a series of automatics and concluded that although none were as brutally reliable as a revolver, the Browning designs appeared promising.

Fighting the natives
When the Army fought fanatical tribesmen in the Philippines, American soldiers demanded a very powerful pistol cartridge which would be guaranteed to disable the most ferocious spearman. .38s were not considered sufficiently powerful and in

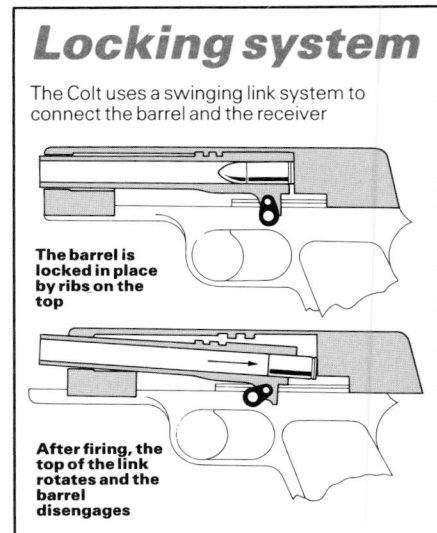

Locking system
The Colt uses a swinging link system to connect the barrel and the receiver

The barrel is locked in place by ribs on the top

After firing, the top of the link rotates and the barrel disengages

Heavy weapons crew still rely on the Colt .45 for personal protection, but the replacement of the M79 grenade-launcher by the M203 has removed the Colt from most US infantry squads.

ifications. In fact Browning more or less completely redesigned the Colt, and by the spring of 1910 this new model was submitted. Army tests throughout 1910 caused the Savage to be eliminated, and more detail work to be done on the Colt, with the final result that on 29 March 1911 the Colt design was formally approved as the 'U.S. Pistol, Automatic, Caliber .45, Model 1911.'

Classic and simple

The Browning design is of classic simplicity, so classic and so simple that it is still appearing on new pistol designs to this day. The pistol consists of three major components, the frame, the barrel and the slide. The slide moves back and forth on rails in the frame, and the rear half of the slide is the breech block, carrying the firing pin and extractor.

The frame consisted of the butt, holding the magazine, the trigger, the hammer, and a grip safety device which prevents the hammer going forward unless the butt is properly held and the grip compressed. The barrel is attached to the frame by a short link

The .45 is a single-action weapon; that is, the trigger merely releases the hammer. This means you must rack back the slide to cock the hammer and chamber the first round.

1904 a series of tests were conducted by firing a variety of different weapons against live animals and human corpses. The Army concluded that only .45 calibre would do and Colt re-worked the design to accommodate this larger round.

Two for testing

In 1906 the Army advertised for pistols in the new calibre to be submitted for testing, but due to delays it was not until early in 1907 that the tests were conducted. These recommended that the Colt and a design by Savage should be given more extensive trials and 200 of each were requested for issue to troops for a solid year of testing in service conditions.

This was completed in 1909 and both pistols sent back for some mod-

The Colt .45 can be carried 'cocked and locked' (hammer back and safety catch on), or hammer down in the half-cock position. Here the hammer is fully cocked and the gun ready to fire.

pinned underneath the barrel at its upper end and anchored to the frame by a cross-pin at its lower end; this acts as a sort of hinge around which the rear of the barrel can swing. The top of the barrel has two ribs machined on it, and these match two grooves in the inner surface of the slide top.

To fire the pistol you insert a magazine into the butt, pull back the slide against a spring which lies beneath the barrel, and release it. The slide runs forward and the edge of the

STRIPPING THE COLT.45

1 Remove the magazine and check that the chamber is clear before pushing down the recoil spring plug with your thumb.

2 Rotate the barrel bushing a quarter-turn while pressing on the plug, then remove both plug and spring.

3 Move the slide group halfway back to line up with the oval opening on the side, and push down the rounded end of the slide stop.

breech block collects a cartridge and pushes it into the chamber of the barrel forward, and the 'swinging link' underneath it causes it to pivot forward and up. As it does so, the lugs on top move into place in the grooves inside the slide top and the barrel and slide are locked together.

The firing process

Pull the trigger and the hammer drops, hits the firing pin, and fires the cartridge. The bullet goes down the barrel and the barrel recoils. In doing so it makes the slide recoil as well, since the two are locked together, so the breech stays firmly closed until the bullet has left the muzzle and the powder pressure inside the barrel has dropped to a level where it is safe to begin opening the breech.

As the barrel moves back it pivots around the link until the lugs are pulled free from the slide recesses. At this point the barrel stops moving, but the slide has been given sufficient momentum, by the recoil, to continue back, extracting the empty case and ejecting it and cocking the hammer by simply rolling over it. Recoil stops, the spring forces the slide back, the pistol reloads and the barrel and slide lock together again. Simple. But remember that it took John Browning from 1898 to 1911 to get it perfect. Not quite so simple as it looks.

Minor changes

After experience with the pistol during the First World War the US Army requested some small changes; the hammer spur was made larger, the curvature of the frame over the firing hand slightly greater, the trigger made shorter and the mainspring housing, at the rear edge of the butt, made curved rather than flat. These improved the handling without changing the significant features, and the pistol then became known as the M1911A1 in 1926. No further improvements were made throughout its

4 Pull out the slide stop and remove the slide group.

Barrel
Note how it locks into slide. It is primarily designed to shoot GI ammo, not lead target loads.

Front sight
This is too small for really effective combat use; it is better to replace it with a high-visibility combat sight if the weapon is your own.

Barrel bushing
This supports the barrel and holds the plunger in place. Target bushings are available on Series 70 Colt Mk IVs and they do improve accuracy, but they have no place in combat shooting as tolerances are too tight for sustained reliability.

Plug plunger
Depress the front end of the plunger, 'the plug', in order to rotate the barrel bushing anti-clockwise at the start of the field strip. This is the piece you are most likely to lose as it is under strong spring pressure.

Inside the Colt.45

This is a life-size cutaway of the Colt .45, the oldest combat pistol still in front-line service all over the world. Now that Congress has over-ruled the US Army's decision to adopt the new Beretta 92, the Colt will have to soldier on a little longer. Whatever the final decision of the Army, the Colt is already back in production by popular demand.

service life, and today Colt still manufacture to the same pattern for commercial sale.

Not for the amateur

Firing the Colt .45 is not a pastime for dilettantes; it has a powerful cartridge and when you pull the trigger

5 Remove the recoil spring guide and recoil spring out of the slide group.

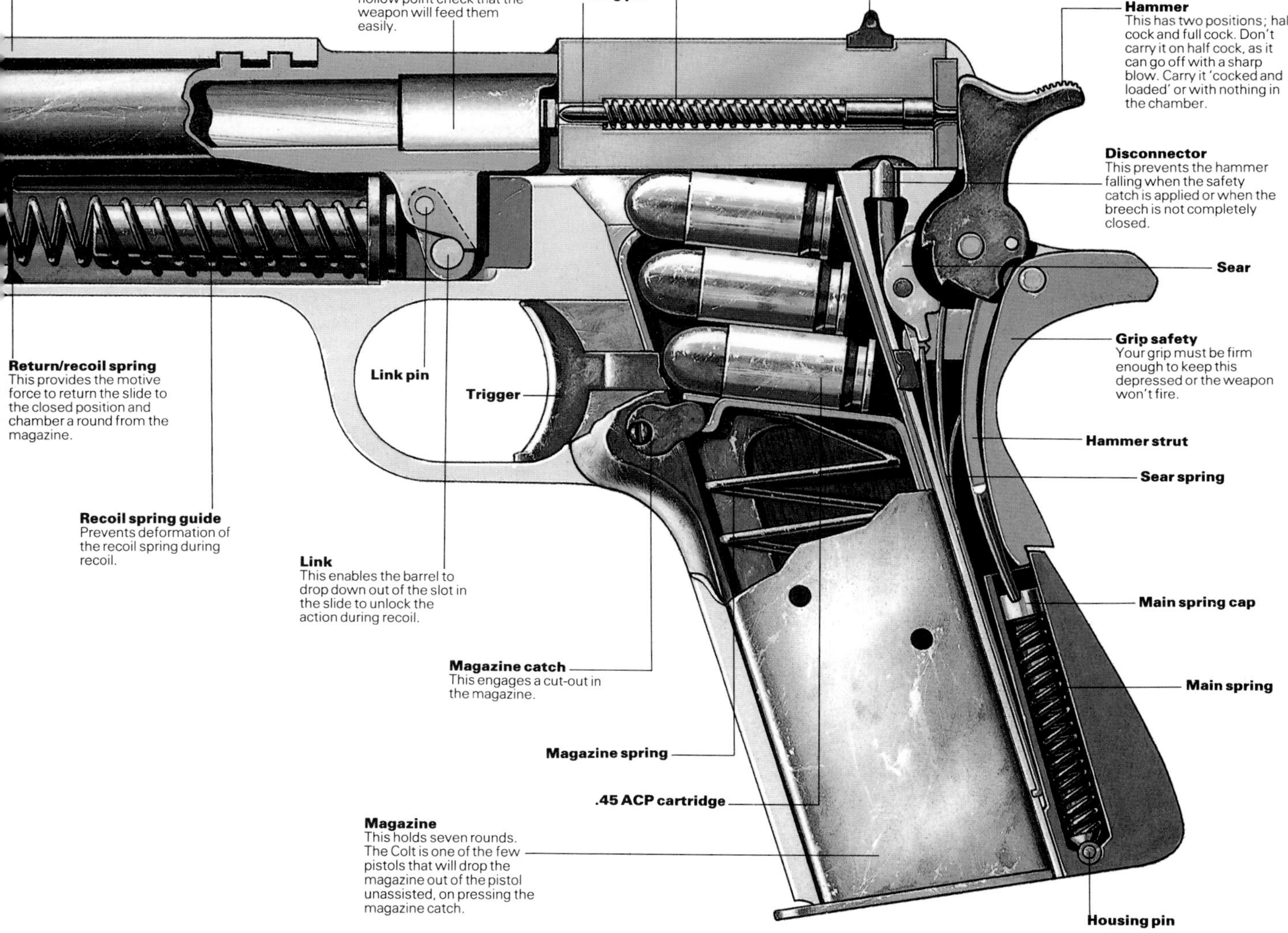

Slide
To cock the weapon, pinch in with the fingers and thumb of the left hand against the serrations on the slide and rack it firmly to the rear and release.

Chamber
Stoppages are rare with the GI issue full metal jacket ammo, but if you use expanding ammunition types such as semi-jacketed soft point or hollow point check that the weapon will feed them easily.

Firing pin

Firing pin spring
This returns the firing pin to position after firing.

Rear sight
Again, this does not provide a good sight picture as issued.

Hammer
This has two positions; half cock and full cock. Don't carry it on half cock, as it can go off with a sharp blow. Carry it 'cocked and loaded' or with nothing in the chamber.

Disconnector
This prevents the hammer falling when the safety catch is applied or when the breech is not completely closed.

Sear

Return/recoil spring
This provides the motive force to return the slide to the closed position and chamber a round from the magazine.

Link pin

Trigger

Grip safety
Your grip must be firm enough to keep this depressed or the weapon won't fire.

Hammer strut

Sear spring

Recoil spring guide
Prevents deformation of the recoil spring during recoil.

Link
This enables the barrel to drop down out of the slot in the slide to unlock the action during recoil.

Magazine catch
This engages a cut-out in the magazine.

Main spring cap

Main spring

Magazine spring

.45 ACP cartridge

Magazine
This holds seven rounds. The Colt is one of the few pistols that will drop the magazine out of the pistol unassisted, on pressing the magazine catch.

Housing pin

---

you are left in no doubt that you have just touched off a .45. Because of this it takes a good deal of time and a good deal of ammunition before you reach a competent level of skill and a lot more of both before you become really expert. As a combat pistol it is highly regarded simply because of its re-

6 Put your finger through the ejection opening, push up on the barrel, and slide it out of the front end of the slide group.

7 Completed field strip: give the barrel a good scrub and use a powder solvent to clean it before lightly oiling. Check the breech face is clean and make sure the magazine chute and feed ramp are also free from fouling.

liability and its awesome stopping power; hit somebody with a .45 and he immediately loses interest in the argument.

Minor drawbacks

In the eyes of the experts it has its drawbacks; the magazine only holds seven rounds – you can get another one into the chamber, giving you eight in the hand; it is a single action gun, which means that either you carry it unloaded and have to pull back the slide before going into action, or you

Unlike all its original rivals, the Colt .45 Model 1911A1 has stood the test of time and has become a close-quarter combat legend.

Battlefield Evaluation: comparing

Colt .45 M1911A1

The Colt .45 is the most widespread pistol in the world but its design is over 70 years old and it makes better sense to compare it with contemporary rivals rather than the latest modern weapons. Matched against modern automatics the .45 suffers from a small magazine capacity and, since it is a single-action gun, you have to pull back the slide to chamber the first round. However, against contemporary pistols the .45 measures up very well indeed, which is why it has outlasted all but one.

Specification:
Cartridge: .45 Automatic Colt Pistol
Weight: 1.35 kg loaded
Length: 219 mm
Barrel length: 127 mm
Magazine: 7-round box

Assessment
Reliability	★★★★
Accuracy	★★★★
Age	★★★★★
Worldwide users	★★★★★

The 'knock down' power of the Colt .45 has ensured its continuing popularity over the last 70 years.

Browning 9mm GP35

This was Browning's improvement on the M1911 pattern, in which he used the cam to unlock the breech instead of the link, and a double-row magazine gave it 13 shots to the Colt's seven. Over the years the Browning High Power has proved itself just as reliable as the .45 and many armies have adopted it as standard. Had the Americans decided to change to 9 mm 20 years ago they might well have adopted the Browning since it merely perpetuated the old design.

Specification:
Cartridge: 9-mm Parabellum
Weight: 1.04 kg loaded
Length: 200 mm
Barrel length: 118 mm
Magazine: 13-round box

Assessment
Reliability	★★★★
Accuracy	★★★★
Age	★★★★★
Worldwide users	★★★★★

The Browning 9 mm is a development of the original system used in the Colt and an equally successful pistol.

9-mm Luger

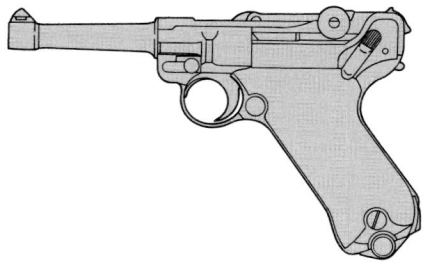

The Luger is elegant, famous and has attained the status of a collector's piece, but as a combat pistol it has always been outranked by the Colt. In spite of being the official German service pistol from 1908 to 1938 and soldiering on until 1945, the fact is that the Luger was sensitive to ammunition variations because of its delicately-balanced toggle breech, had a terrible trigger pull and was vulnerable to dirt clogging it up.

Specification:
Cartridge: 9-mm Parabellum
Weight: .87 kg unloaded
Length: 222 mm
Barrel length: 103 mm
Magazine: 8-round box

Assessment
Reliability	★★
Accuracy	★★★
Age	★★★★★
Worldwide users	★

The Luger was a valued war trophy in both world wars but as a combat pistol it is outranked by the Colt.

load it, leave the hammer cocked and put on the safety, and the experts frown on both these concepts today; it's heavy; and the sights are scarcely up to target standards.

Add that to the training problem and you see why the US Army is trying to adopt a modern double-action 9-mm pistol with a 15-shot magazine. But there are an awful lot of people in America who feel that a 9-mm bullet isn't going to stop arguments with anything as certain as the finality of a .45 slug.

On the right is a Gold Cup, the 'Rolls Royce' of Colt .45 competition pistols. Left is its nearest rival, the Smith & Wesson model 745.

the Colt with its rivals

Walther P38

This was the official German pistol during World War II and is still in production today under the designation P1. Its advantage over the Colt is that it is a double-action weapon, allowing a quick first shot, and its mechanism was more robust and tolerant of poor ammunition than that of the Luger. On the other hand, it fires 9-mm Parabellum, which lacks the stopping power of .45 ACP despite its higher velocity.

Specification:
Cartridge: 9-mm Parabellum
Weight: .96 kg loaded
Length: 219 mm
Barrel length: 124 mm
Magazine: 8-round box

Assessment
Reliability	★★★★
Accuracy	★★★★
Age	★★★
Worldwide users	★★

The Walther P38 used by the Germans in World War II is still in production today under the designation P1.

Radom wz 35

The official Polish service pistol from 1935 to 1939, the Radom was not much more than the 1911A1 brought up to date. Like the High Power, it used Browning's improved method of unlocking the breech by using a cam rather than a link. It is a heavy weapon that fills the hand and makes for a steady shot, and it certainly rates as one of the best 9-mm combat pistols. The Germans manufactured it until 1944 but the post-war Polish army adopted the Russian Tokarev, so few were produced by comparison with the Colt.

Specification:
Cartridge: 9-mm Parabellum
Weight: 1.02 kg loaded
Length: 197 mm
Barrel length: 121 mm
Magazine: 8-round box

Assessment
Reliability	★★★★
Accuracy	★★★★
Age	★★★
Worldwide users	★

The Random was yet another development of the Colt .45, modernised and firing 9-mm Parabellum.

7.62 mm Tokarev TT-23

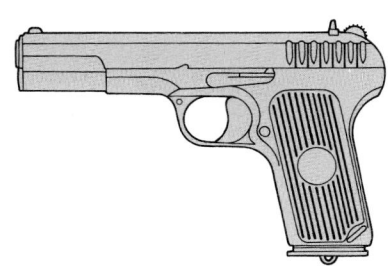

The Soviets developed the Tokarev from the Colt .45 design during the 1920s and it was the Red Army's standard automatic pistol during World War II. A single-action weapon, it retains the Colt's swinging link system of operation, although the lock mechanism and safety arrangements are different. In the Soviet tradition, it is a very tough weapon indeed, but its 7.62-mm cartridge is not a match for .45 ACP.

Specification:
Cartridge: 7.62 mm × 25 Tokarev
Weight: .85 kg unloaded
Length: 195 mm
Barrel length: 116 mm
Magazine: 8-round box

Assessment
Reliability	★★★★
Accuracy	★★★
Age	★★★★
Worldwide users	★★

The Soviet Tokarev was also developed from the Colt, but its 7.62-mm × 25 round is weak compared to .45.

Evasion and Capture

To be taken prisoner is the worst thing that can happen to a soldier. Death is quick; a wound will see you evacuated to a field hospital for treatment; but capture exposes you to a nightmare of torture, indoctrination and exposure. An army is a part of a nation, an arm of government, and every government goes to great lengths to protect its soldiers from every danger, including that of mistreatment as a prisoner of war.

What to do

The United States Army issues Field Manuals – FM 21-76 and FM 21-78 – that deal only with evasion, escape and survival. This section is taken from those manuals. It deals with evading enemy forces and how to behave if you're captured. Later sections will tell you how to hold the line under interrogation, and how to cope with life as a prisoner.

The manuals put a new word into the English language – the evader. A man, probably on his own, being hunted by enemy troops in unknown country. The chances against him are enormous, but if he keeps his head

and remembers his training, he just might escape – against all the odds. Evaders are split into two types: short-term and long-term.

Short-term evasion

You're a short-term evader if you or your unit is temporarily cut off from the main body of your forces. This can happen quite frequently while you're on patrol, for instance, and is actually the way of life of long-range patrol units (known as LURPS in the US military).

When you know you're going to be separated from the main force, navigation and fieldcraft are your best friends. Knowing where you are and which direction you're heading in is going to help save your life, and your own skill at moving cross-country or through a town will finish the job.

9 points for successful evasion

1 Large groups are easily detected. If there are a lot of you, split into four-man teams, which are harder for the enemy to detect.

2 As long as you are wearing your uniform you can attack enemy military targets, but not civilians.

3 Do not disguise yourself as a local unless you do so convincingly. Amateur disguises and ignorance of local language and customs will quickly betray you.

4 If you landed by parachute, you should assume that the enemy spotted your descent and get out of the immediate area as fast as you can.

5 Observe the basic rules of camouflage,

concealment and movement at all times.

6 Take your time when travelling: hurrying makes you less alert and tires you out.

7 Avoid populated areas and busy routes wherever possible. If approached by strangers pretend to be deaf, dumb or just half-witted. It often works.

8 If you are being helped by the local population, do not make any marks on your map: if you are captured with it the enemy could work out who was assisting you.

9 Observe enemy troop movements, military positions, weapons and equipment if you have the chance – but do not write anything down, or you risk being treated as a spy.

Long-term evasion

Very few people have to evade the enemy for long periods of time or cross long stretches of enemy-held territory. The only people likely to have to undertake this most difficult and arduous task are aircrew who have been shot down, and escaped prisoners of war, though patrols are sometimes sent so far out that the same principles apply to them.

Try to relax. Fear and tension will only force you into making mistakes. Time is on your side. It doesn't matter how soon you get back to your own people, as long as you do get back.

This may mean lying up for weeks or even months, and applying all your survival skills.

Under United States law, a soldier must make every effort to return to his unit. If captured, it is his duty to try to escape – though very few ever do so successfully. Getting 'home' will be a lot easier before you're captured. You must use all the tricks of camouflage and concealment to stay hidden from the enemy.

On your own

Rely on your own resources. Don't trust civilians unless you absolutely have to. Their whole way of life will be strange to you. A gesture that in your home town might mean "welcome" could mean the very reverse in enemy territory.

It's not a good idea – ever – to try to disguise yourself as a native. Even if your colour and clothes don't give you away, and you happen to speak the language, the smallest gesture will be enough to show an experienced obser-

Rejoining your unit

If you're out on patrol, there will be an established method of rejoining your own forces – directions of approach, safe periods, recognition signals, passwords and all the other ways of making sure that you don't come under fire from your own people. If you do, by chance, get cut off from your unit, you won't have the benefit of these safeguards, so you must follow basic rules when rejoining:

1 Get in a position close to the front line.
2 Watch and wait for a friendly patrol.
3 Let them come to you.
4 Don't give away your position – or that of the patrol – to enemy forces.
5 Show a white cloth
6 Shout out an unmistakable greeting
7 Don't fool around. The patrol will believe you're the enemy trying to trick them until you prove otherwise.

If you get caught without map, compass or other navigating equipment, use your memory. Orient yourself by listening to the fighting. Use your time behind the enemy lines to gather intelligence. Take a prisoner if you think you have a reasonable chance of making it back to your own lines with him. You must think positively all the time. Fear is your worst enemy.

Shot-down aircrew often find themselves a long way behind enemy lines, faced with the prospect of long-term evasion and probable capture. If the enemy find you, your most dangerous moment will usually be at the moment of capture when the enemy soldiers are excited and pointing guns at you. Stay calm, and move slowly.

A US soldier surrenders to North Vietnamese troops in South Vietnam. It is said that you are less likely to be shot on the spot when trying to surrender if you get rid of your helmet first.

ver that you're not what you're pretending to be.

If you have been lucky enough to make contact with a friendly local group, be guided by them – but remember that no conventions of war apply to them. Any civilian found helping you will probably die for it.

Take every opportunity to distance yourself from your helpers. If you have to travel with a member of a local resistance group, for instance, don't sit together. Arrange a system of simple signals so that you don't have to speak.

Be ready to go it alone at any moment, and don't carry anything that could point a finger of suspicion at anyone who might have helped you. No names and addresses written down; no marked maps. Remember

that you're a representative of your country – perhaps the first one the natives have actually met. Even under the hardships that an evader must endure, it's up to you to make a good impression. Remember, you're fighting a war so that these people can live in freedom.

Communicating

If you do get the chance to talk to natives and feel secure enough to ask them for help, communicating is going to be a big problem. The chances are you won't speak each other's language, so you'll be reduced to making signs and gestures. To make this easier, the US Government issues each soldier with what is known as a "Blood Chit". A Blood Chit is an American Flag, printed onto cloth, with a message in English and all the other languages you are likely to come across in the area in which fighting is taking place. The last, and most important, feature of the Blood Chit is a

unique number that identifies the person it was issued to.

The message asks for help and assistance. It promises that this will be rewarded. Don't give up the Blood Chit itself. Any one who helps you will get their reward just by quoting the number. Give them the number but don't give up the chit itself.

Take care of the chit

If you lose your Blood Chit, report it straight away. It's a very valuable document. If it falls into the hands of the enemy's Intelligence Section, they could very easily use it to discover which members of the local population are likely to be friendly to you, and this will probably get them shot. It will certainly make sure that no-one trust the chit – or you.

It may be possible for your own people to rescue you, most likely from the

Searching and handling a prisoner
This is how you can expect to be treated by an enemy who 'plays by the rules'.

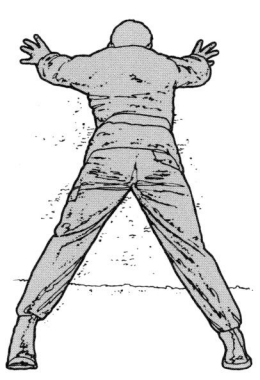

1 Standing position: arms stretched, body relaxed. They work from top to bottom and will check your clothing carefully.

2 Stress position: with your weight on your fingertips and toes, you cannot react quickly. Expect your groin and armpits to be checked as well.

3 If you are caught in a group they may position you like this to prevent fast reaction against the search.

4 Again, if you are in a group, you will be placed close together and your captors will not move between you.

air. To stand a chance of this being successful you must know the standard ground-to-air distress signals.

Don't call down a rescue attempt unless you are absolutely sure that the area is safe. Remember that a helicopter is most vulnerable to attack when it's taking off and landing. Make sure that any signals can be removed or covered up very quickly in case an enemy air patrol should appear.

Save the wounded

If there are casualties, make sure that they get off first. If you do have seriously wounded men in your party, you must always consider whether their best chances of staying alive are to surrender (United States law allows that). Obviously, local conditions will be important — a man with a light wound surrendering to troops who are known to kill all prisoners, de-

Royal Marines of the Falklands garrison surrender to the Argentine Buzo Táctico Marine Recce unit. When captured you are obliged to give your name, rank, number and date of birth only.

spite the Geneva Convention, is not helping himself!

Intelligence of all sorts — and evidence of the bloodthirstiness of enemy troops is only one sort — is really vital. Use every means you can to learn about enemy troop movements and placement and the attitude of local non-combatants.

Stay aware

Try and keep abreast of the progress of the war as a whole, too. You may be hiding for nothing! Remember that some Japanese infantrymen were still living concealed in the jungle of the South Pacific islands 25 years after the end of World War II, because they didn't know it was all over.

If the worst does happen and you face capture, your first decision will

According to Radio Hanoi, a US Air Force pilot was captured by a North Vietnamese militia woman. In a one-to-one situation you may be able to escape, but he (or she) who has the rifle may have the last laugh.

be whether to try and fight your way out. If you're alone and unarmed, this is not likely to be an available option, but if you're with your unit and your armament is up to strength, you may stand a very good chance of winning a fire-fight even against a larger enemy force, because surprise will definitely act in your favour — the last thing the enemy force will expect is an armed and trained group of soldiers behind its own lines.

If you are captured, you are required to tell the enemy only four things — your name, rank, serial number and date of birth. Say nothing else. Don't refer to your unit by name, don't talk about your superior officers, don't identify the leaders of your group. The smallest piece of additional information may be useful to the enemy.

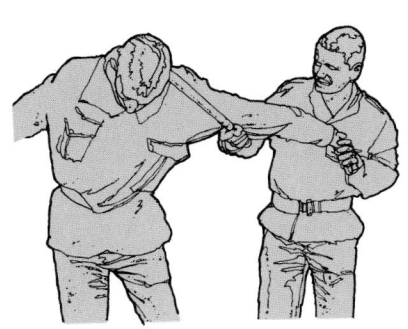

5 A two-man arrest position: one fixes you with an armlock while the other applies pressure points.

6 One way of using a baton to support an armlock: with the baton under your arm and behind the neck you are immobilised.

7 Arresting method with a baton: by pushing this between your legs and grabbing you by the neck, the guard can move you easily by pushing your neck and raising his right arm.

Under Interrogation

To the army on the move, taking prisoners is more than a waste of time, it's a waste of precious manpower to guard them and rations to feed them. It's often only some respect for the laws of warfare and the fear that they would be treated the same way themselves that keeps them from shooting everybody.

To the intelligence specialist, though, the prisoner is not a waste of time. He's precious. He may be pure gold. The information about troop strengths and positions that he has in his head – perhaps not even realising that he has it – could be the difference between a battle lost and a battle won.

The US Army knows this, and spends a lot of time training its men how to combat enemy interrogation techniques. Field Manual FM 21-76 is the source for this section on how to get through a hostile interrogation while giving away as little information as possible.

THE INTERROGATOR'S SKILL

The laws of war

The news of your capture is supposed, under the Geneva Convention, to be passed to a body called the Protection Power, often the Red Cross/ Red Crescent, so that they can pass it on to your own government. That's the only reason for giving away even

US prisoners are herded through the North Vietnamese capital, Hanoi. These public displays were used to prey on the emotions of the prisoners' families in America and turn public opinion against the war.

such simple information as your name, rank, number and date of birth.

If you're captured by a terrorist group, they probably won't do this –

The interrogator prepares himself before interrogating his prisoner. He adopts a three-phase approach:

1 Research
He gathers all the information he can about all his prisoners.
2 Selection
He chooses which prisoners to interrogate and determines the information he wants.
3 Extraction
He puts into operation his varied mix of extraction techniques.

1 Intelligence
The interrogator studies any information he may have acquired from initial searches, overheard conversations, and background material gleaned by intelligence workers operating in the captive's own country.

2 Weak or strong?
He also builds up a picture of the PoW's makeup: is he weak or strong? Can he take punishment? What gets to him? Is he cool or emotional? How has he adjusted to PoW life?

3 Softening up
You'll be softened up, either by rough treatment, starvation, thirst, sensory deprivation, sleeplessness or solitary confinement. The interrogator will set up the place where he'll ask his questions so that it's intimidating and unfriendly.

4 Disgrace
He will try to destroy your confidence by disgracing you in the eyes of your fellow prisoners or your family or comrades at home, or will simply try to make you feel ashamed of yourself.

5 Lesser of two evils
The captor will give you a choice between two evils, one of which is less damaging than the other. He knows that you will choose the least damaging, and that is the one he can use for his own purposes.

Forcing co-operation

These are some techniques that PoWs have been subjected to in recent times.

1 Torture
Technique: extreme dislocation of body parts e.g. arms, legs, back etc by twisting or pulling; beating, slapping, gouging, kicking; inserting foreign objects such as bamboo slivers under the fingernails; electric shocks
Effect: crippling; partial or total temporary or permanent loss of use of limbs and senses; loss of normal mental functioning; extreme pain; lowering or breaking of ability to resist captors' demands
TORTURE IS THE MAJOR MEANS OF FORCING COMPLIANCE

2 Threats
Technique: threats of solitary confinement, non-repatriation, death or beatings to oneself or other PoWs; threats regarding future treatment; threats against family
Effect: unreasonable anxiety; loss of hope and confidence; despair

3 'Now and then' treatment
Technique: occasional favours such as release of food packages and better living conditions; promise of big rewards for helping captors
Effect: tempts the PoW to go along with captors; presents the captors in a favourable light; makes resistance to questioning seem a bad idea

4 Isolation or solitary confinement
Technique: total or partial isolation by rank, race, degree of compliance etc; or total solitary confinement
Effect: keeps PoW away from anyone who can give any kind of support – moral, physical, psychological

5 Hints that captors are in full control of everything in camp
Technique: use of information from other sources to make PoW believe the captors know more than they really do
Effect: makes PoWs suspicious of each other and makes resistance seem futile

6 Show of power over life and death
Technique: use of executions or torture; introduction and withdrawal of better conditions and medical care; complete control over physical aspects of camp
Effect: breeds extreme caution and the belief that the captor is boss

7 Deliberately-caused physical deterioration
Technique: extremely long interrogation sessions; long periods in leg irons and stocks; bad food
Effect: drastic lowering of resistance to interrogation

8 Enforcement of minor rules and commands
Technique: overly strict demands for compliance with instructions and expected courtesies; forcing PoW or write or verbally repeat nonsensical words and phrases
Effect: causes automatic obedience to commands

9 Lowering of self-respect of PoW
Technique: lack of privacy; ridicule and insults; prevention of washing; keeping living conditions filthy, insanitary, full of vermin etc
Effect: humbles PoW and makes giving in an attractive prospect

10 Control over physical senses
Technique: placing in isolation with no stimuli or giving extreme stimuli such as no light or sound, or too much light or sound; dripping water on forehead
Effect: makes PoW think that captors have total physical control; causes extreme discomfort and distress

---

even some governments don't, which is why so many US prisoners of the Viet Cong and Pathet Lao are still recorded as MIA (Missing In Action) following the war in South East Asia.

You don't have to tell them what branch of the service you're from, though they may be able to guess that themselves from your uniform and equipment. Some personnel traditionally get a hard time, notably members of Special Forces units and fliers.

Try not to get noticed and singled out for interrogation. Don't exhibit bravado or humility. Just fade into the background.

Be polite

There's no point in not being respectful and polite – in fact, to behave in any other way is extremely stupid. It will only earn you harsher treatment and probably get you beaten up and deprived of food.

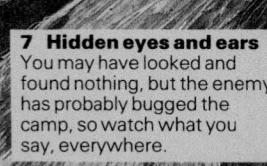

7 Hidden eyes and ears
You may have looked and found nothing, but the enemy has probably bugged the camp, so watch what you say, everywhere.

8 The silent treatment
You may be put into solitary confinement or held in a room with an interrogator who says nothing. Don't be afraid of silence; come to terms with it.

6 The File
Your interrogator may start by asking you a harmless question about yourself. If you give a false answer, he checks his intelligence file on you and gives you the right one. You begin to think, "This guy knows everything. What's the use of holding out?" Don't give in. He is telling you the little he does know. If he knew everything he wouldn't have to question you further.

9 Repetition and monotony
Your interrogator may ask you the same questions in the same tone over and over again. Let him. If you get riled he'll win; if you maintain control the psychological victory will be yours.

10 What's the use?
"Why hold out?" "Why suffer?" "You are at our mercy." "We'll get the information out of you anyhow." "Make it easier on yourself." These are all statements that you must learn to resist.

The Geneva Convention

The Geneva Convention is an international agreement first formulated in 1864 to establish a code of practice for the treatment of wartime sick, wounded and prisoners of war. These are the major elements of the Geneva Convention as it effects prisoners of war.

1 Interrogation
A PoW is required to provide only his name, rank, service number and date of birth. The use of physical or mental coercion to obtain information from PoWs is prohibited.

2 Movement
PoWs must be moved under humane conditions.

3 Environment
The internment environment must not be unhealthy or dangerous.

4 Food
Food must be of sufficient quality and quantity to maintain good health.

5 Clothing
Suitable clothing must be provided.

6 Health, Hygiene and Wellbeing
The detaining power must ensure that adequate hygienic facilities are provided. The PoW is entitled to treatment by medical personnel from their own country, where available. The seriously wounded or sick are entitled to special treatment and may be transferred to a neutral nation.

7 Protected Personnel
Captured medical personnel and chaplains are treated as protected personnel and are to be free to circulate among the PoWs tending to their spiritual welfare and health.

8 Religion, Recreation, Education and Exercise
Each PoW has the right to practise his religion, and to engage in physical exercise, education and recreation.

9 Work
All enlisted personnel below NCO rank are subject to work details, but these shall not be dangerous or unhealthy. NCOs may be called upon to work in a supervisory capacity; officers may work voluntarily. The Geneva convention prohibits the use of PoWs for mine clearance and lays down working conditions, pay, fitness for work, and the treatment of PoWs working for private individuals.

10 Outside Contacts
PoWs have the right to write to their families on capture. The convention outlines postal privileges and rights pertaining to the receipt of packages.

11 Complaints
PoWs have the right to complain to the military authorities of the detaining powers, and to representatives of the neutral protecting powers recognised by both sides.

12 Representatives
The senior PoW will be the prisoners representative. In a camp where there are no officers or NCOs the representative will be chosen by secret ballot.

13 Legal Proceedings
PoWs prosecuted and convicted for offences committed before capture retain the protection afforded by the convention. They may not be tried for any action which becomes illegal after the act is committed. The captors may not use force to gain a confession.

14 Punishment
Cruel and unusual punishments, torture, collective punishments or unfair punishments by a biased court are prohibited.

15 Escape
Attempted escapes, or non-violent offences committed only to aid escape and not involving theft for personal gain, the wearing of civilian clothes or the use of false papers, are subject only to laid-down disciplinary action.

This communist propaganda photograph was used to illustrate 'heroic' North Vietnamese troops who have just captured a shot-down American airman. It is impossible to avoid your captors taking photographs of you.

medical attention for someone badly wounded and not treated properly, or almost anything else that seems attractive. After all, they can promise you anything – you're not going to get it, anyway.

The double game

As well as trying to convince you that other prisoners have been co-operating, he will try to get information from you about them, which in turn will allow him to put subtle pressures on anyone you talk about. Don't give out any information about

At the same time, don't give the interrogator the idea that you might be willing to co-operate. All you'll succeed in doing is to prolong the interrogation.

There's a world of difference between acting ignorant and acting dumb. The interrogator may say something like 'We know there's a build up of troops at such-and-such a location. Does it contain armour?' If your answer were, 'I don't know, Sir, I've never been in that location,' it sounds a lot more convincing than 'Piss off'. But beware of seeming to be trying to be helpful.

Watch out for apparently innocent enemy personnel such as doctors, nurses, orderlies and cleaners. Never talk in front of them; they could well be intelligence agents operating undercover – perhaps not even revealing themselves to other enemy agents on the spot.

Solitary confinement or keeping you in tiny cages preys more on your mind than on your body. Psychological torture leaves no obvious scars, which would beg awkward questions at a press conference.

The enemy interrogator will be very keen to turn you into a collaborator, too. The two main methods are threats – of physical torture or death, to you or to another member of your squad, or promises – of better treatment,

If the enemy forces you to co-operate by using torture, do not give up hope of further resistance. Consider each time you are forced to give in as one round in a long fight. You may lose some rounds but the fight is still open.

any of your comrades. Don't admit to being in the same unit with them.

Be on guard

Watch out for false questionnaires "for the Red Cross", for instance. The aid organisations need to know nothing more than your name, rank, number and date of birth. Any information you provide in a form like this is only for the enemy intelligence officers' use.

Never make any statement of any kind. Not in writing, nor spoken where it might be recorded.

The big shot

Don't try to impress the interrogator by boasting about things that you and your unit have done – whether they're true or not. He's not going to let you go because you make yourself out to be some sort of superman!

At the same time, don't try to deceive him by volunteering false information, no matter how subtly you think you do it. He knows the wide intelligence picture and will recognise your lies, and will ask you the same questions over and over again, perhaps with days in between. He'll record everything you say, and look for differences in your answers.

Don't look into the interrogator's eyes. You may give away information without meaning to. Pick out a spot between his eyes or in the centre of his forehead and concentrate on that.

Once he has you talking, it won't take a skilled interrogator long to get the truth out of you. Don't put yourself into a position where you find that you're having a conversation with him. Let him do all the talking, and limit your answers to "No," and "I don't know anything about that".

Never drop your guard. You can be taken off for further interrogation at any time, at any hour of the day or night.

Victories

Try to win a victory every time you're interrogated, no matter how small. Having worked out how, pass it on to your fellows so that they are

morally stronger.

The longer the interrogation goes on, the safer you are. More prisoners will be arriving and needing your interrogator's time, and your information will become more and more out of date.

What will prolong the nightmare is your partial co-operation. One snippet of useful information will convince your interrogator that he may be onto a good thing, and he'll carry on until he gets the lot, no matter what it takes.

Using this picture, the North Vietnamese were able to say 'Look how nice we are to the US prisoners'. Be on your guard against tricks like this.

Fighting Fit

THE ROYAL MARINES SNIPER COURSE

"A sniper is an infantry soldier who is an expert marksman and observer with the ability to locate an enemy, however well concealed, and then stalk or lie in wait to kill him with one round. He is able to observe, interpret and accurately report enemy movement. He can observe without being observed — and kill without being killed."

As you can see from this official description, to become a sniper you must master a number of skills. Sniping does not simply mean being an expert shot. Equally important are your abilities at stalking, judging distance, observation, concealment, map reading and recording information. To achieve these skills you must be a very special type of soldier, and the Royal Marines conduct what is probably the toughest, most professional sniper training in the Western world.

A variety of recruits

The six-week programme is open to all members of NATO's armed forces, and a course can include not only Royal Marines but also applicants from the Army as well as other European and American volunteers. A typical course might consist of up to a dozen professional soldiers who will be instructed by four members

Playing Kim's Game

The Royal Marines run the toughest and most rigorously professional sniper course in the Western world. Sniping calls for a certain type of personality. You will have to work alone for long periods in adverse conditions. You must be of above average intelligence, decisive, self-reliant and possess plenty of common sense.

Royal Marine Sniper Kit

Donning a purpose-made sniper's hat: it breaks up the distinctive 'head and shoulders' silhouette. You don't need much scrim on your front because when facing the enemy in an upright position the scrim on your sides should break up your outline.

Applying some face veil to the binoculars stops the sun glinting off their reflective surface, and again hides what is otherwise a familiar shape.

Camming up the L96 rifle while wearing a custom-made smock. Loops of elastic or dark string can be fitted for securing local vegetation to your suit. Footwear is a matter of personal choice: civilian hiking boots are common, as are soft-skin desert shoes.

All equipment has to be camouflaged. Rifles and binoculars can have their shape disguised and reflective surfaces (other than optics) dulled with scraps of hessian and issue OG towel. Make sure you don't interfere with the rifle's working parts and that you can remove it all for cleaning.

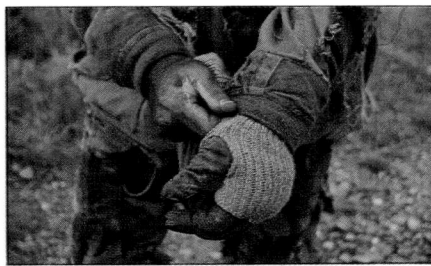

A large splodge of cam cream ready for application. Some candidates use American style multi-colour face camouflage, but others prefer simple black cream. It's up to you, but your camo must be excellent to impress the instructors.

Hide your watch beneath a wristband or simply extend the sleeves of your smock to cover the wrist area with an old sock top or similar. Note the wool mitten over the leather glove.

of the Royal Marines Platoon Weapons (S) Team: usually a Warrant Officer, Colour Sergeant, Sergeant and Corporal.

You should ideally have served at least two years with your unit before volunteering for sniper training. Having volunteered, you will probably then have to pass a selection test conducted by your unit.

No smoking

Ideally you should be a non-smoker. An ill-timed smoker's cough could lead to death, and to stop smoking for the duration of an operation could cause nervousness and irritability, lowering your efficiency. Obviously you must have perfect eyesight: spectacles are an unnecessary liability. Apart from the reflective hazard to camouflage, their loss or damage could put you out of action. Besides being suited emotionally, mentally and physically to your role, you must excel in all aspects of soldiering, from fieldcraft to shooting. Every good shot is not necessarily a sniper, but every sniper has to be a good shot!

If you can convince your superiors that you have what it takes, then you stand a chance of joining other hopefuls at the Specialist Training Wing of the Commando Training Centre Royal Marines, at Lympstone in Devon.

Your first day will be spent in the administration that always follows the move to a new unit or camp. This takes most of the day, but the last two periods (80 minutes) are set aside for introductory lesson to your new weapon, the L96 A1 sniper rifle.

You will be lectured on its characteristics and shown how to strip, assemble, load and unload the weapon. Next day you will be instructed in holding, aiming and firing the L96, and the technicalities of sight adjustment and bore sighting. As in all aspects of sniper training, you learn all there is to know about the subject and then spend several weeks putting theory into practice, perfecting your skills until they become second nature.

Kim's game

This exercise is not really a game: it is the start of a sniper's training to observe and mentally record what he has seen.

During an initial exercise, 16 objects are laid out on a landscape target on a table. You get 30 seconds to view the objects, during which you are marched around while an instructor asks irrelevant questions and a radio

Fighting Fit

You are trained to observe using standard ×6 prismatic binoculars. Objects are deployed on the ground to your front and you must locate and identify them.

plays music to distract your attention. Then you are sent outside for a run around the block, and lastly you get five minutes to write down what you can remember.

You are expected to provide a detailed description of each object. If you saw a pencil, you have to write down the colour and the manufacturer's name. Sometimes, as an added distraction, the objects might be laid out on a map or even on the centrefold of a men's magazine, or your five minutes' writing time might be enlivened by a Wren (WRNS) parading in a negligee!

The rest of your first week is largely devoted to more weapon training and lessons in marksmanship. You will be shown how to use your rifle sling as a means of steadying the L96 during aiming and firing, and also as a support for the Scout Regiment Telescope which, along with your prismatic binoculars, is one of the sniper's major aids in observation. By the end of the first week you will have learned to carry the L96 while on the move, and how to adopt the most suitable of several tried-and-tested firing positions when you reach your objective.

Air photography

Also in the first week you will be introduced to the world of air photography in relation to map reading. A baffling monochrome montage of shapes and angles has to be interpreted for what it is: a bird's eye view of a given area. As a sniper you will, with practice, be able to read air photographs as easily as you would an ordinary map.

Another skill is that of camouflage and concealment. You will already be quite proficient in this art, but you very quickly realize that as a sniper you have to become expert at blending in with your surroundings. To this end you should already have prepared yourself a ghilly suit.

Ghilly suit

A ghilly suit consists of a camouflage cap, jacket and trousers, to which has been stitched pieces of face veil ("cam scarf") and strips of brown, beige and black hessian ("scrim").

The scrim should cover your headwear and much of the jacket, especially at the back, and your trousers, concentrating on the back of your legs from the thighs down. The scrim on your jacket should be long enough to cover the upper thighs.

Having survived joining week, you

When you spot something with the binoculars, use the Scout ×20 telescope for a more detailed examination. Great emphasis is placed on being able to observe accurately.

are dismissed for the weekend. If you are sensible you will take this opportunity to perfect your ghilly suit and brush up on anything you're not completely confident of. The standards set by the Royal Marines instructors are daunting, and only the most professional applicants will pass out as trained snipers. It is a serious business, with no room for mistakes.

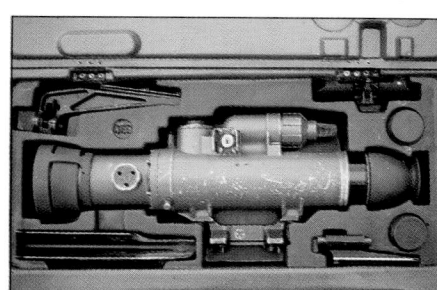

The IWS (Individual Weapon Sight) is an essential aid to night vision. As the course progresses you will be set observation exercises of progressive difficulty which will tax the most eagle-eyed would-be sniper.

Interpreting air photography must become second nature. You will be taught how to interpret aerial pictures until you can read them as well as a map.

Combat Report
Rhodesia:
Hunting the Terrorist

Frank Terrell, who served with the Rhodesian Light Infantry, describes a terrorist-hunting action in early 1979.

Fifteen of us were paradropped one morning into a cultivated area near Inyazura in east Rhodesia. As soon as we landed, our stick of four men hastily formed up and prepared for helicopter uplift to where a suspected terrorist had been seen going to ground.

The Alouette G-car arrived within moments and before long we were deployed along the edge of a ploughed field, facing a thick clump of bush that bordered a small kraal. Our CO, Major Haydock, circling above in the K-car (command chopper), radioed that the terr was definitely hiding in the bush. It was our job to flush him out.

It is frightening to have a hidden armed aggressor watching you, and even more so when you have to go in and find him. Such an exercise almost always resulted in the killing of the enemy, but he was likely to be desperate and doubly dangerous.

A muffled bang

In an attempt to avoid going in personally, we decided to try to dispose of the terr by the easiest method available. Our gunner, Mick Maitland, took up position on the left of our line. Beside him the stick leader, Lieutenant Williams, crouched with his FN rifle aimed towards the bush. To the officer's right, myself and Lance Corporal Kurt Strasser levelled our own FNs. On a command from Lieutenant Williams we all opened up together, sending a stream of fire into the thicket. We waited and watched. Nothing.

Doubting that anyone could have survived, I volunteered to put a grenade into the target area for good measure. I stood up and walked the 30 metres or so to the bush and peered in. I couldn't see anyone. Pulling the pin from an HE grenade, I aimed for a likely hiding place and tossed it in. I then doubled back to the others, arriving just as the grenade detonated with a muffled bang. Dust, twigs and leaves were thrown into the air. That was all. The terr had to be dead, or so badly wounded as not to be a threat. Nevertheless, we again shot up the area and again paused to observe the result. Still no sign of life.

Major Haydock was now running short of patience and ordered us to move into the bush to clear it. Lieutenant Williams told Strasser and

Peering into the bush. It takes a bold man to stride into the scrub in pursuit of an armed terrorist. Reconnaissance by fire was a routine tactic but not guaranteed to score a hit.

myself to take up a new firing position next to a dirt track that ran along the right of the thicket, towards the kraal. This we did, kneeling by the path, keeping the officer and Maitland in view on our left while observing the length of the brush stretching away to our right.

A cloud of dust erupted

The K-car again ordered Lieutenant Williams to move in. Strasser and I watched him and Maitland stand up and spring across the clearing towards their objective. They had almost covered the distance when the air was rent with automatic fire. A cloud of dust erupted, all but hiding the men from view. Green tracer (ours was red) richocheted from the field, high into the sky. Both men had fallen flat as soon as the shooting had started, but it was impossible to tell if they had been hit or were just taking cover.

The firing suddenly stopped. Out of the corner of my eye I saw Kurt stand up and run towards some boulders off to our left. Simultaneously, less than 10 metres away, a shadowy figure flitted past, almost invisible in the thick vegetation. There was no time to take proper aim. Raising my rifle to my shoulder, I squeezed off round after round, following the target until it disappeared. I then flung myself into the dirt and fumbled in my jacket webbing for a fresh magazine. My hand was shaking so much that I couldn't change magazines fast enough. I thought, "The hell with it," and leapt to my feet to join Kurt in cover some 50 metres distant.

Mick was still lying where he had fallen. Lieutenant Williams turned up after a short while, having withdrawn into some bush before eventually creeping across to our position. It transpired that Mick had taken a round in the head and chest and was killed outright.

We didn't know how many terrs had opened fire on us, so to play safe we requested assistance and two sticks were promptly ferried in, one G-car landing close to Mick's body, enabling it to be recovered. Our men then withdrew into cover while a pair of Cessna Lynx aircraft were called in. These subjected the bush to a devastating barrage of frantan (napalm) bombs. A G-car joined in with its twin Brownings, while those of us on the ground concentrated our firepower against the terr's last known position. Finally, with the bush ablaze, the two recently arrived sticks swept through the area and pronounced it clear. The only evidence of the terr's presence was a pile of spent 7.62-mm cartridge cases.

There now followed hours of hut clearing while we searched for the fleeing terrorist. It seemed that other sticks in the area, flown in by

G-car, were also having their share of action, as frantan strikes and bursts of firing kept erupting all around. Soon the skyline was filled with pillars of black smoke from burning kraals. This type of operation was always a vicious, unpleasant business, all the more so whenever one of our number had been killed.

At the end of the day our stick, now reinforced by a replacement gunner, Koos Bessler, was detailed to sweep across a patch of shrub-covered land in search of a wounded terr, thought to be the same fellow who had escaped earlier.

We were carefully following the course of a dried-up river bed when I spotted some equipment lying in the sand. I told Lieutenant Williams that I was going to check it out, and approached what seemed to be a bloodstained shirt on top of a canvas ammunition pouch. I was wondering if the abandoned kit was likely to be booby-trapped when Koos and Strasser called out that they were about to clear by fire: routine procedure, where suspect bush was fired into before approaching.

Strasser leapt for cover

They opened up and were met with return fire from someone concealed only a couple of metres away! Strasser promptly leapt for the nearest available cover and Koos stumbled into the gully next to me. He was clasping his neck and shouting that he had been hit. As Strasser scrambled up the other side of the bank I placed several rounds in the direction of where I assumed the gook to be – a large bush up on the bank to my front right. At that range the foliage exploded in a blur of leaves and dust, temporarily obscuring my vision. Something rolled out into the open: a body, I thought. But it was just some large stones dislodged by my rounds. The terr had managed to get away once again.

Koos was luckily not seriously wounded. Reinforcements were quickly helicoptered in so that they could assault the thicket into which our gook had fled. While our own stick attempted to close on the terr in a flanking movement, another group under the command of an Australian NCO succeeded in locating the man. A short, sharp firefight ensued, followed by the unmistakable report of a detonating grenade. We got up and moved into the open, and linked up with the other stick beside a body sprawled beside an AK rifle. There could be no doubt. The terrorist was dead at last.

A frantan (napalm) bomb dropped from a Cessna Lynx explodes with spectacular effect. Close air support was essential to enable small units of the security forces to defeat the terrorists.

Fighting Fit

THE ROYAL MARINES SNIPER COURSE

During the next four weeks you learn the seven key skills you need as a sniper. Then in week 5, 'Badge Test Week', you will be thoroughly tested in everything you have been taught.

One of your most important skills will be the ability to melt unseen into your surroundings. Concealment alone is simple to achieve, but as a sniper you are required to be able to see and shoot without being seen. But the requirements of camouflage and concealment are not consistent with the need to be able to move freely and use your weapon, so you must compromise between these requirements.

Applying camouflage

You already know about the ghilly suit and the most basic rules of "camming out". But while a mistake in camouflage during basic training would have brought a sharp rebuke and an invitation to complete 10 press-ups, continued negligence during sniper training will guarantee that you will be failed in your final assessment, if not before!

Darken exposed skin with camouflage cream. Check that the camouflage is secure around your rifle and equipment. When using foliage make sure that it matches that of the country

you are moving across. If the vegetation alters, change your camouflage accordingly. And never, ever use a piece of natural camouflage with the roots showing uppermost. This kind of carelessness will not be tolerated during sniper training.

Examples of concealment

Without the correct use of cover, your camouflage will be wasted. Develop the instinctive ability to use cover: sensible use of shadow and background is very important. During

training you will have to demonstrate your ability to blend with the terrain while a pair of sharp-eyed instructors observe for the slightest sign of any disturbance of the countryside. An instructor advises:

"It takes a while to figure out, but the ideal hiding place is in shadow. A sniper can stand or sit virtually in the open if the shadow is deep enough, but it does take some getting used to. At first you just feel vulnerable because you're not lying behind any obvious cover, but binos can't pene-

The course is briefed by one of the instructors prior to a stalking exercise. You will try to sneak up on a group of instructors equipped with binoculars: this is a tough test of your stalking abilities.

Blending with your surroundings

It is difficult to illustrate the way in which a trained sniper can blend with his surroundings to become invisible to his intended target. Here an instructor moves back into some light woodland and begins to merge with the foliage. The instructors stress that it is often movement that attracts the observer's eye and gives away your position. Hiding in shadow takes some getting used to: with no real cover between you and the enemy it makes you feel exposed, but it is the best way of concealing yourself.

Having planned your route with the aid of an aerial photograph, you add local camouflage to your ghilly suit. As the vegetation changes you modify your suit to match it.

trate shadow, so it's really one of the best positions to be in.''

Be aware of your silhouette by avoiding skylines and breaking natural straight lines. When using soft cover, try to observe and shoot through it, not over the top.

Once in position, keep still. Often the slightest movement can give away your position.

Avoid isolated cover. It is difficult to move to or away from, and its isolation serves as a natural attraction to enemy forces.

Other points to consider include having an unobstructed field of fire. A tiny, seemingly insignificant twig or even a few blades of grass can be enough to cause a bullet deflection and a miss. Remember too that you will be watching your target through a telescope sight: the barrel of your rifle will be some three inches lower than the sight itself. Failure to take into account muzzle clearance can be fatal when you're behind a fallen log, wall or similar cover: your first round (and probably your last) will smack harm-

lessly into your immediate cover! Finally, make sure you have pulled through your rifle barrel with a clean piece of flannelette. Oil in the barrel will cause smoke to be discharged upon firing, and will provide the enemy with an excellent aiming point.

Stalking

The purpose of stalking is to move, undetected, to a fire position within range of your target to ensure a first round shot to the head, and then withdraw unseen.

Before stalking, the ground should be thoroughly reconnoitred. Opportunities to view the ground will be rare in battle, so you must read maps and air photographs to obtain the maximum information. Prior to the stalk, you must know:
1 The enemy's position, including nearby features and landmarks.
2 The best possible area for your fire position.
3 The line of advance and withdrawal, taking into consideration the availability of cover; obstacles; observation points along the line of advance; enemy locations; and the general method of movement to be employed.

Bear in mind, too, that the withdrawal route should differ from the approach route if at all possible.
During the stalk you must:
1 Maintain your sense of direction at all times.
2 Remain alert.
3 Observe with care, and at frequent intervals.
4 Decide on the action to be taken if surprised or exposed during the stalk.
5 Be careful not to disturb wildlife.
6 Avoid unnecessary risks.
7 Note and react to any changes in local cover.

Fighting Fit

You move out at dusk on the first leg of your journey on the stalking exercise. The terrain is lightly wooded to start with, but thins out to gorse bushes as you approach the instructor team.

Passing the first tests

During training you are regularly tested on your stalking skills. At the end of Training Week 1 you will be handed a small aerial photograph of the stalk area, the information of which is transferred to a corresponding map. The target is pointed out, but the line of advance is left entirely up to you.

Separating you from your goal is 450 metres of woodland, soon thinning out to gorse bushes about 200 metres short of the objective. The objective/target in this case is a pair of instructors comfortably sitting in deckchairs on the side of a gentle slope. They are each equipped with binoculars and a radio set and will be watching for any sign of approaching snipers. Two more instructors are designated as "walkers". Their task is to follow the radio instructions of the observers, who will lead them towards anything remotely resembling a stalking sniper.

Hidden firing

To pass the test, you must approach to within 150-250 metres of the objective, move into a shooting position, and fire a round without being seen. One of the walkers will then point out your position to the observers while you fire a second shot. If, after that, you still cannot be seen, you've passed!

The initial move out from the start line is relatively easy; the woodland enables you to walk upright for much of the way. But as you approach your objective and the wood changes to a gorse-covered plain, you have to get down on all fours and finally crawl on your belly. Gorse bushes cling and tear at your clothing. You try to ignore the pain as the cruel thorns cut your hands and face. You console yourself with the knowledge that if you can cope with this kind of terrain, anything else should be simple.

On their hill the two observers use their binoculars to scan the area below. They have mentally recorded any obvious folds in the ground, likely bushes, fallen logs; anywhere, in fact, that might hide a sniper.

Telltale signs

After familiarising themselves with these features they periodically check to make sure they haven't altered. A dark shadow in the centre of a light-coloured bush, or a clump of gorse protruding from the side of a tree, may indicate a sniper's presence. It isn't long before the first sniper is spotted, quickly followed by another, and another. An observer depresses his radio switch.

"Okay, Phil, I think I've got a sniper. He's off to your right; turn right, will you? Advance . . . stop . . . one pace forward . . . another pace forward . . . stop. There's a sniper in the bush immediately to your front."

"Roger. What gave him away?"

"Movement. He blends in quite nicely but it was movement that gave him away."

In fact, most of the snipers are soon spotted. You will learn from your mistakes. As the stalks become progressively more difficult, you must in turn become more and more proficient.

A sniper employs the 'Monkey Run' movement technique as he closes on the waiting instructors. Patience is the name of the game, but somehow most men on the course are spotted by the instructors.

An instructor zeroes in on a sniper spotted by the observers. This is where you really learn, and by discussion with others whose positions are discovered you begin to recognise the errors that can betray your whereabouts.

Finally you arrive in your firing position, check your sights and fire. You have to get into position and fire a shot without being seen. Then an instructor reveals your position to the observers and you fire another shot. You pass if they cannot see you for themselves even after your second round.

Combat Report
Oman:
22nd Special Air Service Against Rebels

A former member of the SAS describes an operation in Oman to help put down a rebellion against the Sultan in the late 1950s.

In November 1959 D Squadron, 22nd Special Air Service, were sent in great secrecy to aid the Sultan of Oman in his war against rebel tribesmen.

The rebels, descendants of Quarra Mahra (The Bloodletter), were more than a match for the small and badly-equipped Sultan's force, despite British assistance in the shape of the Lifeguards. From their Djebel Akhdar stronghold high up in the hills they attacked, laid mines and then melted into the safety of the mountain.

We learned much at the hands of the rebels – born warriors whose Lee Enfield rifles were deadly at over 700 metres. They were well equipped with 81-mm mortars and .5 Browning machine-guns, which outranged our 3-in mortars and .30 Brownings.

One day in December found our section of 18 Troop lying up at 900 metres on the west of the mountain, route-seeking and probing the rebel defences. We had gone to ground before daylight, and during the morning had listened to our sister troop, 17, having a private war; they were out of our reach on the other side of Wadi Tanuf, and we sat tight.

The target took shape

At noon our binocular look-out spotted a possible rebel HQ about 1,000 metres away: undetected, we had found a back door to a part of their defences. The boss, De Bill, weighed it up and quickly organised a plan of attack.

The briefing was classic SAS style. We were to be strengthened by the rest of our troop, and, at dusk, a six-man patrol with a Browning .30 cal machine-gun would infiltrate the rebel sentries to be in position to strike at their HQ at dawn. After the attack the patrol would escape under covering fire from our present position and an air strike by Venom aircraft.

My oppo Ben and I were the crew on the 3.5-inch rocket-launcher and didn't join in the "who's going" guessing game; we quietly got on with checking our 7.62 SLRs and ammo. I had four rockets to play with and we would carry them, as usual, 'ready use'.

I'd grown to love that rocket-launcher; it was heavy, clinked when you moved and had a

The main British contingent assisting the Sultan's rag-bag army was drawn from the Lifeguards. This is one of their Ferret armored cars.

ferocious backblast that gave away your position – at night the crew would be clearly silhouetted when it went off. But to my mind all this was outweighed by its warhead, which delivered one hell of a punch.

The rest of 18 Troop linked up at dusk, and on a perfect moonless night we went over the edge at 2200 hrs. We had seven hours to do the distance, and found we needed every one of them.

The boss led us on, skirting known and suspected rebel sentries. We all had great faith in our "lucky" boss, and by the time dawn was breaking we took up position close to the rebel HQ.

Ben very softly slipped a rocket into the tube while I strained through the sight at the target area. No picture yet.

As the light improved, the target took shape: a fortified cave with sangars (small fighting positions made from piled-up rocks) to the left, right and over the top. The cave would get the first rocket, and I needed a live target to give me the range.

At that moment a rebel appeared, his silver ammo belts glinting in the sunshine. I set the sights for 150 metres; although the range was shorter, I had to allow for the thin air.

It was up to the boss now. Rebels appeared, seeming to grow out of the ground; there was a shot to my left, and 'Silver Belts' went down in one. I squeezed off, and misfired. I missed a double heartbeat. Ben drew, slung, and reloaded. This one went smack into the cave and hit something special, because half the mountain came back at us.

The Venoms arrive

A left and right at the sangars, both catching rebels in the blast, left us out of rockets. Now we grabbed cover and joined in the firefight; we were taking fire from all angles, and when our supporting fire dropped short among us there was no point in hanging about.

Then the Venoms, unheard until the last moment, came in with rockets on their first pass. Then they did a cannon run, strafing the rebel positions and showering us with spent 20-mm cases. Stunned, deafened and cut by flying rock splinters, we legged it at impossible speed while the Venoms 'sheepdogged' us back to our supporting fire.

The troop was taking accurate fire and was down to its last metre of Browning belt when we scrambed in, and they waved us through as we headed for our old OP.

The locals: loyal tribesmen today, rebels tomorrow! With old British Army Lee-Enfield rifles they were incredibly good shots and an enemy to be respected. They operated from the Djebel Akhdar stronghold in the hills.

The Venoms gave us a wing wag and were gone. We paused on the way down to give covering fire against snipers that wouldn't let go, and we were soon down to loose ammo in our pockets. The lower slopes gave our mortars the chance to shield us with a barrage of phosphorus bombs, which we were glad of.

Weary, and realising with relief that we'd got away with it this time, the boss de-briefed us in the safety of the desert. The kills we could only guess at for the moment; the Sultan's spies would feed us the gen on that later.

'Silver Belts' turned out to be their chief armourer, and our first rocket had apparently taken out an 81-mm mortar crew, ammunition and all. Enemy dead was reported as between 18 and 23.

We deserved a rest but, typical SAS, we never got one. Months later the rebel stronghold was captured and I went up to examine the site of the action. It was a scene of utter destruction and the mass grave of a breed of warriors who gave no quarter and asked for none.

Bits of local dress proved popular for both colour and comfort. We used a great mixture of weapons, including this World War II Bren gun.

Fighting Fit
THE ROYAL MARINES SNIPER COURSE

An Eye for Ground

As a professional soldier, you must be able to read a map quickly and accurately. As a sniper, you must learn to understand an aerial photograph as proficiently as any map. You must also become an accurate judge of distances and a skilled observer. These skills will enable you to record and relay vital information in an efficient, reliable and professional manner.

Map reading

The first step in reading any map is to orientate yourself. Find the direction North, and align your map accordingly. You can do this by using the compass, or by lining up your map in relation to prominent features visible on the ground. Then you can easily work out your own position.

However, an ordinary map is often insufficient for a sniper to work from. Even Ordnance Survey maps can quickly become dated: buildings are demolished, others are built; woodland and other vegetation is cut down, and paths and roadways change. For a sniper to have an up-to-date plan of an area, regular aerial photographic missions are flown to provide the latest information.

Recent photographs

Before beginning a task, you will be issued with recent air photographs of the operational area to be used with your map(s). You will use two types of photograph – one taken from the verti-

Using the Scout Regiment Telescope

Your primary means of observation is, of course, your own eyes. To be a successful sniper you do need good eyesight: glasses are an unacceptable handicap. You use the 20 times magnification of the telescope for detailed study of areas of interest. Telescopes provide the best results only when properly supported; here an instructor demonstrates various methods of obtaining a steady view.

Using telescope case

Resting on a tree

cal, providing a similar picture to your map, and the other shot at an oblique angle.

You will undergo several mapreading/air photograph exercises. The exercises are similar but the problems become progressively more difficult.

Using air photographs

You will find yourself positioned on high ground, surrounded by a panorama of forested hills and sweeping plains. The instructor will allocate you a position and then outline the first problem.

"Last night you were dropped by parachute in the areas easting 04-06, northings 85-87. The enemy are operating in the north and you have been given the task to locate and establish an OP, and to observe and report any enemy movement in the arc north of your east-west line.

"The first thing I require is that you establish your own position on both air photographs and map. It will help if you find and mark the direction north on your photos once you have orientated yourself. All right, gentlemen, you have ten minutes . . . "

Behind you is a wood running to a small clearing on the top edge of a hill. You are in this clearing. Below you is another wood, a fir plantation. It is in a valley where pale brown, open grassland covering rolling hills that stretch away to your left and back beyond the wood, to merge on the right with the green, reddish-brown and bright yellow patterns of cultivated land.

Dotted here and there is an occasional copse. The hills reach to the horizon, on which you can see several clumps of woodland. The only sign of habitation is a small farm in the valley two o'clock of your position, and one or two other more distant buildings.

You orientate yourself with the aid of map, binocular, prismatic and Silva compass, protractor and ruler. You look for features and landmarks which might be recognised and identified on the air photos. Then you carefully mark them on the air photographs as an aid to gridding the vertical-angle picture so that it corres-

All dressed up and nowhere to go. You must master the art of precise navigation using aerial photographs if you are to succeed as a sniper. The map reading and air photography lessons become progressively more difficult during the third week of the course.

Using the rifle, kneeling

Using the rifle, standing

Using the ×6 magnification binoculars

Judging distances is not easy. When asked to judge the distance to the bottom right corner of the fir tree plantation, visible just above the head of the centre man, estimates varied from 620 to 1000 metres. The true range is 920 m.

ponds to the same area on your map.

Ten minutes later, your allocated time is up. You present your answer to the instructor and are marked accordingly. Others might need some help before being set another problem to solve. Ask about anything you are uncertain of: there will be no time for errors during Badge Test Week.

It takes practice to read a one-dimensional black and white picture taken from several hundred metres. Yet within a couple of lessons you will have grasped the essentials and be able to relate your surroundings to both map and air photograph with equal ease.

Observing

Your introduction to observing and recording information began with your first Kim's Game exercise. By course week one this has progressed to your initial outdoor observation stance, during which you will scan a piece of ground to your front for 40

On your initial outdoor observation stand the objects on the left are hidden up to 100 metres away. To give an idea of the difficulty, the main picture was taken from the obs stand and one item has been pinpointed. The other eleven are all on there too!

minutes, recording anything of interest. In this first test you must locate at least eight out of 12 objects partially concealed amongst the grass, trees and bushes, up to a distance of 100 metres.

You will use the standard issue prismatic binoculars (×6 magnification) to scan the area. If anything suspicious is observed, the Scout Regiment Telescope (×20 magnification) can be used in order to get a better look.

With the binoculars, divide the ground into a foreground, middle distance and far distance. Starting with the foreground, observe by scanning a horizontal pattern, overlapping slightly as you move up into the middle distance, and finally the far distance. If the area appears to be clear, scan such features as ridgelines and hedgerows etc, along and away from your position. Get into the habit of looking *into* any likely cover rather than *at* it.

Make detailed notes of anything of interest. You will be provided with a panoramic photostat of the observation area upon which to mark the items seen. Later on you will be expected to keep an accurate log sheet and draw a sketch of the observation area yourself. Be as concise as possible when recording information: you will have learned the importance of detailed and accurate note-taking during Kim's Game sessions.

In outdoor observation exercises you must be just as methodical. The information you record will be relayed to others who might be many

At the observation stand: somewhere to your front are 12 objects, and you have 40 minutes to locate them. In later exercises you won't know how many objects have been hidden or what they are.

miles from the operational area. The failure or success of an operation and the lives of others may well depend on your reliability.

Determining your position by resection

The resection method is used to determine your position on a map. After orientating your map, look for at least two prominent landmarks and use your compass to take a magnetic bearing to each of these.

Next, convert the magnetic bearing to a back bearing. This is achieved by subtracting 3200 mils from your magnetic bearing if it is more than 3200 mils, and by adding this amount if the magnetic bearing is less than 3200 mils.

Then convert the back bearing to a grid bearing by subtracting the magnetic variation. Use a protractor to plot the bearings from each landmark on your map and your position will be where the two bearings intersect.